the Forth Naturalist and Historian

Volume 26 2003

Published by the Forth Naturalist and Historian, University of Stirling – charity SCO 13270 and member of the Scottish Publishers Association. November, 2003.

ISSN 0309-7560

ISBN 1-898008-53-1

Supported by BP in Scotland.

Cover: front– Lampreys, River Devon (photo P.S. Maitland).
    back– *The Honble Mrs Graham*. Thomas Gainsborough 1775. National Gallery of Scotland.

Printed by Meigle Colour Printers Ltd., Tweedbank Industrial Estate, Galashiels. Set in Zapf Calligraphic on Edixion 100 gsm and cover Aconda Gloss 250 gsm.

CLIMATIC CHANGES AND THE NATURAL HERITAGE OF SCOTLAND

Noranne E. Ellis

Introduction

At the end of the last Ice Age in Scotland

Evidence from the last Ice Age, such as fossilised remains in soil, indicates that around 10,000 years Before Present (BP), the climate of Scotland rapidly became warmer. Land denuded by the ice sheet began to be colonised by grasses and sedges. It took a few hundred years for vegetation to cover Scotland, with small shrubs such as crowberry (*Empetrum nigrum*), juniper (*Juniperis communis*) and willow (*Salicaceae*) appearing over this time. Birch (*Betula* spp.) was one of the first colonisers and the first dominant tree to expand its range to the far north of Scotland, achieving this within approximately 1,000 years of the disappearance of the ice sheet (9000 years BP) (Peglar, 1979). Hazel (*Corylus avellana*) occurred with the birch in the lowlands.

It took a further 1,500 years (8,500 years BP) before oak (*Quercus* spp.), elm (*Ulmus* spp.) and Scot's pine (*Pinus sylvestris*) invaded the birch-hazel stands across southern Scotland, the central lowlands and along the west (Walker and Lowe, 1997). At this time (the late Holocene), fossilised beetle remains indicate that the mean annual temperature across southern Scotland had dropped from around 9°C (the maximum temperature during the Late Glacial Interstadial and Holocene) to about 5.5°C (Atkinson *et al.*, 1987). In comparison, the current mean annual temperatures of Glasgow and Aberdeen are c. 9°C and c. 8°C respectively.

Between 5,000-4,000 years BP cooler, wetter conditions occurred and peatlands became extensive whilst tree cover declined (Price, 1983). January and July mean monthly temperatures were possibly 1°C and 5°C higher, respectively, than at the end of the Ice Age (Bishop and Coope, 1977), and total annual precipitation had possibly increased to a level about 10 % greater than that recorded during the mid-twentieth century (Price, 1983).

Climatic changes across Scotland

Climate changes across Scotland have been caused by two main factors. Firstly, the positioning of the Earth, its orbit and tilt relative to the sun, which is believed to be a major contributory factor to the historical glacial and inter-glacial periods across the globe. Secondly, the effect of the ocean current, the Gulf Stream, bringing warmer waters to the British Isles has affected the regional climate. At the end of the last Ice Age, the most dramatic climatic changes experienced across Scotland have been related to alterations in the flow of the Gulf Stream.

Whilst slight fluctuations in the Scottish climate have occurred over the last thousand years, and most likely related to the regional influence of the Gulf

Stream, none of these fluctuations have been of the same order of magnitude as those at the end of the Ice Age. However, between 1860 and 2000, the global average surface air temperature increased by $0.6 \pm 0.2°C$ which is likely to have been the largest for any century during the last thousand years in the northern hemisphere (Folland *et al.*, 2001). Europe experienced the upper range of this warming of 0.8°C (Beniston and Tol, 1998) with the 1990s likely to have been the warmest decade of the millennium (Folland *et al.*, 2001).

Significant alterations have also occurred in precipitation patterns, both spatially and seasonally. A comparison of the mean rainfall within the period 1960-1990 to that between 1940-1970, indicates that there was a general increase during the winter half-year (in some locations to as much as 20 %) and a decline during summer months (again, in some locations by as much as 20 %) (Mayes, 1996). Overall, Scotland became wetter, particularly in the west, with an increase in the number of days with heavy rain (Smith and Werritty, 1994).

The current accelerated warming of the climate is believed to be primarily the result of increasing concentrations of greenhouse gases in the atmosphere, in particular carbon dioxide (CO_2) (Houghton *et al.*, 2001). Whilst some historical temperature trends have been related to increases in atmospheric CO_2 concentrations, the present CO_2 concentration has not been exceeded during the past 420,000 years, and likely not during the past 20 million years (Prentice *et al.*, 2001). About three-quarters of these emissions arise from the burning of fossil fuels with the rest caused by land use change, especially deforestation.

The annual global mean air temperatures may rise by 1.4°C-5.8°C by 2100 above the mean temperature observed between 1961 and 1990 (Houghton *et al.*, 2001). This is much greater than the 2°C variation over the last 10,000 years (Wheeler and Mayes, 1997). UK models predict a warming of between 2°C and 3.5°C for Scotland by the 2080s (Hulme *et al.*, 2002). At the same time, the total annual precipitation may increase by 5-20 % above the 1961-1990 baseline with summers potentially becoming drier (by between 20-50 %) and winters becoming wetter (by between 10 and >30 %). In summary, the expected rise in temperature is to exceed the maximum observed at the end of the last Ice Age, and the climate is expected to become as wet as 5,000-4,000 years BP. Mean wind speeds are expected to remain much the same with westerly airflows remaining dominant .

General responses by species to climatic change

Climatic factors generally have a great influence on the presence and abundance of species at a specific location although other factors such as physiography, soil and land use may modify the species composition (Hodgson, 1986). Whilst climatic factors include temperature, precipitation, atmospheric humidity and wind speed characteristics, ambient air temperature is usually the main determinant of the limit for spore and seed germination (Larcher, 1983). Precipitation is also a major influence on the limits for most species, with the distribution of global terrestrial biomes (vegetation units determined by their life-form) related to both temperature and precipitation (Whittaker, 1975). At distributional limits, the abundance of a species is generally low because sub-optimal conditions reduce survival rate. An expansion of range is therefore associated with greater rates of survival at the previous limits of distribution. The relationship between the distribution of a species and some aspect of temperature may be related to the attainment of critical temperatures of air and soil, including an attainment of a thermal accumulation (Larcher, 1983) and/or the passing of a chill period, such as required for a number of tree species to produce leaves (e.g. Murray *et al.*, 1989).

The timing of life-cycle events, such as leaf production, is also strongly influenced by temperature but may be modified according to precipitation patterns, such as drought during the previous growing season. Getting the timing right of such events, particularly in spring, can be crucial to the competitive edge of a species. Development too early in the year may risk injury by late frost whilst delayed developments may not allow the full use of the growing season. Even within a species, ecotypes may vary as to the environmental cues they respond to in order to move to the next stage of their life-cycle. For example, some species exhibit different thermal requirements at different latitudes which may have evolved as a response to varying photoperiods. That this is a genetic shift in thermal requirement has been demonstrated by transferring ecotypes that flower early to a different latitude and witnessing the continuance of the requirement for their usual temperature accumulation (Larcher, 1983).

The main issues for habitats and species arising from the current climatic changes

Rapid, large and manifold changes in the environment are likely to produce adverse effects on species and their relationships. Five key issues for habitats and species arising from the current changes in climate are, therefore, (1) disparity between the rate of climatic change and rates of species' dispersal and re-distribution with suitable climate, (2) loss of land with suitable climate from Scotland, (3) disruption in food chain relationships, (4) barriers to dispersal and (5) other physical and chemical alterations in the ecosystem arising from some aspect of climate change.

Disparity between the rate of climatic change and rates of species' re-distribution

The maximum rate that Scots pine (*Pinus sylvestris*) is observed to have extended its northern limits across Scotland 8,500 years BP was by c. 37-80 km per century, with birch (*Betula* spp.) having extended its northern limits by 40-60 km per century 10,000-9,000 years BP. Hazel (*Corylus avellana*) dispersed at a rate of only 20 km per century (Gear and Huntley, 1991). This indicates that the dispersal capability of trees may be restricted to a warming of 0.1-0.3°C per century.

By contrast, a number of bird species extended their northern limits across Britain by 19 km between 1970 and 1990 (Thomas and Lennon, 1999), and northward shifts of butterfly ranges were of the order of 35-240 km over the last 30-100 years (Parmesan *et al.*, 1999). This is associated with a warming of just over 0.1°C per decade (Folland *et al.*, 2001).

Using plant survey records from 70-90 years earlier, Grabherr *et al.* (1994) were able to calculate that the maximum rate of uphill dispersal of alpine plants at around 3,000 m altitude in the Alps was 4 m per decade at best, with most values below 1 m per decade. These rates were linked to a warming of the mean air surface temperature of 0.7°C over these 70-90 years. Assuming a decrease of 0.5°C per 100 m rise in altitude, such an increase in temperature may have caused a shift in altitudinal climate space by 8-10 m per decade.

The loss of land with suitable climate

If species are to remain within their optimal temperature range, for each 1°C rise in mean surface air temperature they would need to be able to shift northwards by 250-400 km and uphill by 200-275 m (derived from Cannell *et al.*, 1997). By the 2050s, assuming a rise of between 1.5°C and 2.0°C across Scotland (Hulme *et al.*, 2002), isotherms may have shifted 375-800 km further north and 300-500 m higher up the hill. For species like the endemic Scottish primrose (*Primula scotica*) with a latitudinal range extending 200 km from the north coast of Scotland to the north of Orkney, the new location of suitable climate space may be within the Arctic ocean (Figure 1). In Scotland, arctic-alpine species are likely to lose 90 % of their habitat.

Disruption in food chain relationships

The growing season across the British Isles extended by 21 days between 1970 and 1999 (Rötzer and Chmielewski, 2000). This has been related to an increase in the mean air surface temperature in spring of 0.5°C across Scotland between 1960 and 2000, the equivalent of bringing forward the spring growing season by around ten days (S.J. Harrison, pers. comm.). Examples of earlier springtime events in Britain related to an increase of 1°C in temperature include tree species coming into leaf earlier by 5-7 days (Sparks and Carey, 1995), robins and chaffinches laying their eggs earlier by 3 and 2 days respectively (Crick, 1999), a 2-3 day earlier arrival of migrants like the swallow (Sparks and Loxton, 1999), and butterfly and moth species appearing 6-10 days earlier (Sparks and Yates, 1997; Sparks and Woiwod, 1999). In East Lothian, earlier flowering has occurred at a rate of about one day per year for species which flower between January and March (inclusive) associated with an increase of 0.7°C between 1976 and 2001 (Last *et al.*, 2003). This varying rate of advancement of springtime events for species in an ecosystem may lead to disruptions in food-chain relationships such as pollinator/flower and predator/prey relationships.

The challenges for nature conservation

Climatic changes observed during the twentieth century caused variations in distribution, abundance and phenology of species in Scotland, but the meteorological changes predicted for the twenty-first century are expected to be 3-6 times greater. Evidence from the last Ice Age also indicates that the rate of species' responses to rapid climatic changes have been much slower. Yet current climate changes are also accompanied by other new challenges such as barriers to dispersal in the landscape such as urban areas and transport routes such as the large motorways across Scotland's central belt. Northern species are expected to retreat north whilst southerly species will and are arriving at ever more northerly sites, leading to changes in the composition of species communities at each location.

Management of areas designated for nature conservation will therefore need to consider which species are not only desirable (in terms of nature conservation), but also the likelihood of loss of some species and the impact of those likely to enter. Further, a number of plant species of conservation value have poor dispersal and reproductive abilities, and are likely to need assistance in their dispersal to new more northerly locations. At some point, international co-operation will be necessary for northern and montane species. Hard choices as to which species, habitats and ecosystems we are capable of assisting to respond to climate need to be made.

The main requirements for those in nature conservation are therefore to consider the likely alterations in the distribution of suitable climate for climate-sensitive and other key species in sensitive ecosystems under various climate change scenarios, the consequences of likely changes in species communities, the dispersal and reproduction of the most vulnerable species, and to produce contingency plans for the management, dispersal assistance, and the monitoring of species, their habitats and ecosystems.

The Forth area

In the next few decades, the central area of Scotland between the Forth and Clyde, is more likely to see species arriving than leaving because it has relatively few northern and montane species and is close to the northern limits of many southern species. For some time, it may therefore enjoy a greater level of biodiversity than currently observed, particularly with the arrival of mobile species like birds and many invertebrates such as butterflies. However, for northward bound species with limited dispersal capability (such as many plant species), the central area with its conurbations and motorways, may become an obstacle to further movement northward. Plans to assist the dispersal of such species northwards across this area may be required.

References

Atkinson, T.C., Briffa, K.D. and Coope, G.R. (1987). Seasonal temperatures in Britain during the past 22,000 years, reconstructed using beetle remains. *Nature*, 325, 587-593.

Beniston, M. and Tol, R.S.J. (1998). Europe. In *The Regional Impact of Climate Change: an Assessment of Vulnerability* (ed. R.T. Watson, M.C. Zinyowera and R.H. Moss), pp. 149-185. Inter-governmental Panel on Climate Change, Working Group II. Cambridge: Cambridge University Press.

Bishop, W.W. and Coope, G.R. (1977). Stratigraphical and faunal evidence for late glacial and early Flandrian environments in south-west Scotland. In *Studies in the Scottish*

Lateglacial Environment (ed. J.M. Gray and J.J. Lowe). Oxford: Pergamon Press, pp. 61-88.

Cannell, M.G.R., Fowler, D. and Pitcairn, C.E.R. 1997. Climate change and pollutant impacts on Scottish vegetation. *Botanical Journal of Scotland*, (49)(2), 301-313.

Crick, H.Q.P. (1999). Egg-laying dates of birds. In *Indicators of Climate Change in the UK* (ed. M.G.R. Cannell, J.P. Palutikof and T.H. Sparks). pp. 64-65.Wetherby: DETR/CRU/NERC,

Folland, C.K., *et al.* (2001). Observed Climate Variability and Change. In *Climate Change 2001: The Scientific Basis* (ed. J.T. Houghton, Y. Ding, D.J. Griggs, M. Noguer, P.J. van der Linden, X. Dai, K. Maskell and C.A. Johnson), pp. 99-192. Contribution of Working Group I to the Third Assessment Report of the Intergovernmental Panel on Climate Change. Cambridge: Cambridge University Press.

Gear, A.J. and Huntley, B. (1991). Rapid changes in the range limit of Scots pine 4,000 years ago. *Science*, 251, 544-547.

Grabherr, G., Gottfield, M. and Pauli, H. (1994). Climate effects on mountain plants. *Nature*, 369, 448.

Hodgson, J.G. (1986) Commonness and rarity of plants with special reference to the British Flora II: the relative importance of climate, soils and land use. *Biological Conservation*, 36, 253-274.

Houghton, J.T., *et al.* (eds.) (2001). *Climate Change 2001: The Scientific Basis.* Contribution of Working Group I to the Third Assessment Report of the Intergovernmental Panel on Climate Change. Cambridge: Cambridge University Press.

Hulme, M., *et al.* (2002). *Climate Change Scenarios for the United Kingdom: The UKCIP02 Scientific Report.* Tyndall Centre for Climate Change Research, School of Environmental Sciences, University of East Anglia, Norwich.

Larcher, W. (1983). *Physiological Plant Ecology.* 2nd edn. Springer-Verlag, Berlin.

Last, F., Roberts, A. and Patterson, D. (2003). *Climate Change? A Statistical Account of Flowering in East Lothian: 1978-2001.* Geography & Environment. East Lothian 1945-2001, pp. 22-29.

Mayes, J. (1996). Spatial and temporal fluctuations of monthly rainfall in the British Isles and variations in the mid-latitude westerly circulation. *International Journal of Climatology*, 16, 585-596.

Murray, M.B., Cannell, M.G.R. and Smith, R.I. (1989). Date of budburst of fifteen tree species in Britain following climatic change. *Journal of Applied Ecology*, 26, 693-700.

Parmesan, C., *et al.* (1999). Poleward shifts in geographical ranges of butterfly species associated with regional warming. *Nature*, 399, 579-583.

Peglar, S. (1979). A radio carbon dated pollen diagram from Loch of Winless, Caithness. *New Phytology*, 82, 245-263.

Prentice, I.C., *et al.* (2001). The Carbon Cycle and Atmospheric Carbon Dioxide. In *Climate Change 2001: The Scientific Basis* (ed. J.T. Houghton, Y. Ding, D.J. Griggs, M. Noguer, P.J. Van der Linden, X. Dai, K. Maskell and C.A. Johnson), pp. 183-238. Contribution of Working Group I to the Third Assessment Report of the Intergovernmental Panel on Climate Change. Cambridge: Cambridge University Press, pp. 183-237.

Price, R.J. (1983). *Scotland's Environment during the Last 30,000 Years.* Edinburgh: Scottish Academic Press.

Rötzer, T. and Chmielewski, F.M. (2000). Trends growing season in Europe. *Arboreta Phaenologia*, 43, 3-13.

Smith, K. and Werritty, A. (1994). *Hydroclimatic and Water Functions of Scottish Hydro-electric plc.* Report to Scottish Hydro-electric plc.

Sparks, T.H. and Carey, P.D. (1995). The responses of species to climate over two centuries: an analysis of the Marsham phenological record, 1736-1947. *Journal of Ecology*, 83, 321-329.

Sparks, T.H. and Loxton, R.G. (1999). Arrival date of the swallow. In *Indicators of Climate Change in the UK* (ed. M.G.R. Cannell, J.P. Palutikof and T.H. Sparks), pp. 62-63. Wetherby: DETR/CRU/NERC,.

Sparks, T.H. and Yates, T. (1997). The effect of spring temperature on the appearance dates of British butterflies 1883-1993. *Ecography*, 20, 368-374.

Sparks, T.H. and Woiwod, S.P. (1999). Dates of insect appearance and activity. In *Indicators of Climate Change in the UK* (ed. M.G.R. Cannell, J.P. Palutikof and T.H. Sparks), pp. 58-59 Wetherby: DETR/CRU/NERC.

Thomas, C.D. and Lennon, J.J. (1999). Birds extend their ranges northwards. *Nature*, 399, 213.

Walker, M.J.C. and Lowe, J.J. (1997). Vegetation and climate in Scotland, 13,000 to 7,000 radiocarbon years ago. In *Reflections on the Ice Age in Scotland - an Update on Quaternary Studies* (ed. J.E. Gordon), pp. 105-115. Glasgow: Scottish Association of Geography Teachers and Scottish Natural Heritage.

Whittaker, R.H. (1975). *Communities and Ecosystems*. 2nd edn. New York: Macmillan.

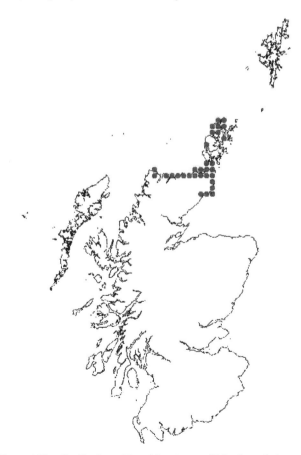

Figure 1 The distribution of Scottish primrose (*Primula scotica*) across Scotland.

BOOK REVIEWS

The Working Countryside in the Forth Valley. Forth Valley. Countryside Initiative. Eds. K. Mackay et al. 2002. 93pp. RHET Royal Highland Educational Trust.

This is an information support pack for teachers – well and clearly presented in five chapters – the farming scene; European perspective; farming today; farming in the Forth Valley; woodland coservation and wildlife; – and appendices, references, and a directory of resource providers. Maps and some features are from FNH'S *Central Scotland – Land, Wildlife, People* which was put in all schools in 1995, and later as a CD Rom HSE – *Heart of Scotland's Environment*.

Saving Butterflies: a practical guide to conservation. Ed. David Dunbar. Butterfly Conservation. 80pp. ISBN 0 9512452 9 5.

Well presented.

Native Woodlands of Scotland. Ransay, Radcliffe et al. Forestry Commission. 24pp. ISBN 0 85538 357 7.

Well presented.

Scottish Natural History Societies and Allied Groups Directory. 2002. BRISC Biological Recording in Scotland. Ed. Anne-Marie Smout et al.120pp.

A Source Book for Biological Recording in Scotland. Eds. Anne-Marie Smout and David Mellor. BRISC, c/o Chesterhill, Shore Ed, Anstruther, KY10 3DZ. 170pp. ISBN 0 9535934 0 1.

Embraces all aspects of biological recording, the collection, processing and use of data, techniques, standards and principles in biological recording, cooperation and data exchange, and where to find out more. A huge amount of information.

The first two sections deal with purpose and techniques, principles and standards of data collection, management and cooperation. The next two – where to find information, both locally LRCs, and nationally via a huge range schemes – their activities, publications, identification guides etc. The final section is concerned with putting information to use through local Biodiversity Action Plans.

Seven appendices give lists of priority species and habitats, useful addresses, books reports papers, legislation, grid referencing, vice counties.

Landscapes and Lives: the Scottish Forest through the Ages. John Fowler. Canongate. £16.69.

A well researched study rangeing from the post Ice-Age natural seeding, through the 'Planting Dukes' era, to the post war plantation years, and the managed commercial and leisure woodlands of today. Includes the oldest Scots pine, oaks of Perthshire, Bailefuil near Strathyre, Loch Lomondside, and Darnaway's in Moray that re-roofed Stirling Castle's Great Hall.

NATURE'S CALENDAR
RECORDING WHEN NATURAL EVENTS OCCUR – PHENOLOGY

Angela Douglas

This paper is based on the presentation to the 28th FNH Man and the Landscape Symposium in November 2002 about a specific project of the Woodland Trust (WT) and the Centre for Ecology and Hydrology (CEH). It explains what Phenology is, describes the Phenology Network, which has a UK wide base, and outlines some of the results from the recording of natural events. It concludes with how this information is being used and how the Network might be developed.

Phenology

Phenology is the study of the timing of natural events, such as flowering, and fruit ripening, not to be confused with Phrenology the study of mental stability by feeling bumps on the head! Natural events specifically relating to climate are selected and people record when these happen in their locality. Events such as horse chestnut coming into leaf or ivy flowering. In selecting the events to be recorded we have tried to identify those which can easily be noted to enable as many people as possible to get involved, whether in the countryside, in the garden, or out of the window, and of all ages and abilities.

Historical events are recorded, and this has unearthed some that are truly wonderful. The earliest from 1703 was in Worcestershire for the first appearances of butterflies and swallows, and for hearing the cuckoo – information extracted from a weather diary. Another is the 150-year-old diary kept meticulously for 50 years by a museum curator in Kent. A recorder contacted us about his father's 38 years of diaries and notebooks.

All records are examined after database entry and Phenology Network is very keen to get records from Scotland, particularly any continuous for 20 years or more, because over this timescale trends begin to become apparent.

Evidences relating to the changing seasons have been occurring for a long time and in fact predate any reference to calendar dates. Examples include a Roman floor mosaic in Kent, and the recordings of first blossoms on cherry and peach trees kept by the Chinese since the eighth century in order to time ancient festivals.

Phenology records can come from a wide range of sources. The Royal Meteorological Society Report on Phenology (a scheme run from the 1890s which sadly ceased in 1947); Robert Marsham considered to be the founding father of Phenology started recording in 1736 and his family continued until 1958 when a neighbour took over and continues to do so; a beekeeping diary 1928 to 1982 giving honey yields; and a card index of observations from West Sussex covering 50 years.

The Phenology Network

The Woodland Trust became interested and keen to be involved with Phenology, as climate change is probably the single largest threat to our ancient woods, which generally are small, fragmented and isolated. One of the great things about the Network is that anyone can take part, wherever they live. It is a good way to help reconnect people with wildlife and the countryside.

Seasonal recording has been taking place since 1736 when the above Robert Marsham began recording his "indications of spring" on his Norfolk estate, so there is a lot to compare current records with. He spent 62 years cataloguing things like the appearance of first leaves on various trees, in order to improve timber production.

People can record on-line or on paper (see the Guide to recording (1). Results can be viewed directly, and compared with the historical, or geographical records. There is live mapping of events such as first appearance of bluebells and the cuckoo; people can see the effect of climate change for themselves. No specific scientific knowledge is required only a observant eye and inquiring mind. The significant spring signs include budburst, first leaves and flowers, first sights of migrant birds, nest building, butterflies, bees, ladybirds, even the first date you cut your grass. Records must come from within a six mile radius of a fixed point such as your home, or school or workplace. People are free to record as much or as little as they can manage. The Illustrated Guide for Spring and Autumn (1) gives much essential information to help people record correctly, and with confidence, as many or few events as they wish (Figure 1).

Phenology Results

Information from the UK Phenology Network is certainly revealing real changes in wildlife behaviour related to temperature. The United Nations Intergovernmental Panel for Climate Change (IPCC) predicts warming of 2.4-5.8°C over the next century. Events are happening on average 6-8 days earlier in spring for each degree increase in temperature. Spring on average is now coming a week earlier than 30 years ago as shown by the dates of oak leafing, snowdrop flowering, house martins arriving and so on. Equally autumn is later, often with an increasing intensity of autumn colours. This is because a longer growing season increases the concentrations of sugars in the leaf. At the end of the season as the chlorophyll breaks down it reveals the other pigments particularly carotene and anthocyanin, both of which are more intense with the increased sugar concentrations.

Research in Germany is showing the same sort of changes with autumn coming later as the climate warms. In southern England the winter squeeze is on, with overlapping autumn and spring events, notable in the case of early primroses and snowdrops. In Britain five of the six warmest years since 1659 have occurred since 1990. Globally nine of the ten warmest years have occurred since 1990, particularly in Eurasia. 1998 was the warmest, with last year, 2002, being the second warmest since worldwide records began in 1860.

Some other examples of results from the records include – daffodil shoots photographed on the first of February each year between 1917 and 1926 show how timings vary; records of oak leafing from Surrey from 1950 to 2001 show how it has become earlier from around 3rd May to 5th April, almost a month, over this 51 year period. Oak leaves fully emerging last year but grouped by location shows that being 800 km further north makes it three weeks later than in southern England.

A comparison of when snowdrops first flowered from 1950 to 2000 in Northumberland and Norfolk, shows this event occurs earlier further south, and the more recent the record the earlier the first flowers appear. Scotland records for daffodil flowering, plotting average temperatures for the first quarter of the year against days January to April, show a clear correlation – the lower the temperature the later the flowering, whilst warmer weather brings about earlier flowering.

One-hundred-and-forty-one years of harvest date records in Sussex show that it is not just native species that are temperature affected. When temperature was not increasing key agricultural events such as harvest times were more stable. Hawthorn is now leafing 17 days earlier around 1st April in Scotland. For birds the arrival of the willow warbler, which has become earlier from about 28th April in 1960 to some 5 days earlier over the last 40-years These examples show the variability of events, and how different species in Scotland have the ability to respond to climatic change.

The Recorders

So who is recording these events now through the Phenology Network? At present we have 19,200 recorders mainly in the over 30 age group (Figure 2) of whom about 1,000 are in Scotland. This makes the UK Phenology Network the largest such recording network in the world. Although we say even one or two records are important, the average number made in Autumn 2002 was an impressive twenty five per person. You can see from the map (Figure 2) that although the coverage is pretty extensive, Scotland, Northern Ireland and Wales have gaps. We would like to see at least one recorder every 10 km grid square. Another important target is to encourage those who have registered as recorders to return their information. At present about 30 % return records, can we make it 50, 60 or even 70 %? We really do need every record to build up as comprehensive a recording system as is possible.

The Woodland Trust (WT) teamed up with the Centre for Ecology & Hydrology (CEH) in 1998 and initially concentrated on establishing a recording system accessible to as many as possible. The first couple of years we narrowed down what we asked people to record, and ensured we had adequate checks and measures in place to have confidence in the reliability of the information processed. We started to really promote the project in early 2001 with quite a lot of success – recorders having grown from 350 in Spring 2001 to 12,300 a year later in Spring 2002. Then 18,304 last autumn and 19,200 at present, around half of these are online representing the largest such recording scheme in the world. There is lots of help on and offline to identify wildlife events and species. There is a website and a free phone number. We are also trialling a children's section called "Nature Detectives".

It is important to recognise that volunteer monitoring is in fact the norm for many natural heritage projects. We stress the importance of not recording if people are unsure of what they are looking at and the date they observed that change. We compare against historical records to establish range checks. Typically we summarise observations for each area, or year, and make comparisons with previous years. Any wild cards/records are picked out and investigated. The numbers of observations are so large that discrepancies have very little influence on averages. Over time the trend in recording and the response if any to temperature are determined by regression analysis, statically treated for significance. This determines how confident we are that the result is real and not an artefact of data collection.

The use of Phenology results and the future

Finally on how we use this information and hope to develop the Phenology Network. The UK basis of the Network enables both national and regional climate change indicators to be identified. From this trends can be identified and reported in a wide range of ways and the information can be used for a variety of purposes. The Forestry Commission for example launched a book last year *Climate change: Impacts on UK Forests*. One chapter is devoted to the role of Phenology in helping to understand the impact of climate change on UK forests. Much of the source data comes from the UK Phenology Network. There have been features in *Nature* and the *New Scientist*, and numerous presentations and lectures. Collaboration is beginning across Europe too. The Dutch Natuur Kalender is hoping to use our software to begin online recording, and interest in how we have used on line is coming from as far away as Australia.

There are direct implications for people – winters are warmer and increasingly frost free with implications for pests (with a knock on effect to agriculture), forestry, leisure, and human health. Longer growing seasons means a longer pollen season, and an increase in related allergies. Hay fever is one of the commonest allergies, affecting about 1 million people in Scotland – youngsters most markedly, 36 % of 12-14 year olds and 25 % of 6-7 year olds. Numbers have risen from 10 to 12 % in 1965 to 15-25 % across the UK today. Grass is the commonest trigger but birch pollen is important too. This spring we are working with the National Pollen Research Unit and it is hoped our records will help to forecast the start and length of the hay fever season.

There is evidence that established dates for some outdoor events, related for example to flowering, are having to be brought forward. There are records of people in southern England mowing their grass all year round!, 4 % of recorders continued throughout the winter, 19 % recorded continuous cutting or first cutting in January/February. Over the last 30 years the growing season has lengthened markedly, by 20-30 days or 3-4 weeks. Spring is arriving a week earlier than 30 years ago and autumn takes longer to set in.

To summarise some key points: Phenology ......

Shows us
- in conjunction with historic data the extent of change and response to temperature
- the popularity of the network scheme and the willingness of the public to get involved
- the viability of web based recording

Does not yet enable us to fully
- identify response to extreme events
- identify problems of competition between species and problems in the food chain
- assess regional variation
- examine possible genetic change in phenology

Conclusion

Phenology is raising more questions than it answers. For example, what species are facing real problems in terms of their ability to move, or adapt to climatic changes? There are problems of synchrony, life cycles and competitive advantage. For every 1°C rise in temperature species need to move up to 250-400 km northward or 200-275 m uphill, or be able to adapt. To illustrate this we know that in the past from pollen samples hazel has moved 20 km/century, birch 40-60 km/century and Scots pine 37-80 km/century. The United Nations Intergovernmental Panel for Climate change (IGPCC) predict a 2.4-5.8°C rise over the next century which means species would need to be able to move some 625-2,320 km northward, or 480-1,595m uphill, or a combination of both if they can't adapt. Prospects don't look good for some of our native tree species.

It is interesting how different species respond in terms of their ability to adjust. Insects such as bumble bees and butterflies appear relatively well able to adapt and appear about 3 weeks earlier than 10 years ago. Flowers generally are about 2 weeks earlier and most birds about a week or less, earlier. An important aspect is the synchrony between plants and animals and there are real concerns relating to this. For example, blue tits nest to coincide with high numbers of looper moth caterpillars that feed on oak leaves. Oak is leafing earlier and blue tits are not adapting as quickly consequently this is having a negative impact on their breeding success. The differing response times lead to some fundamental questions about the future events in life cycles where different species have evolved their life cycles/timings to coincide. The ability to adapt will impact on food availability, competitive advantage and so on.

Autumn is taking longer to arrive, by about a week in the last 10 years. Brambles are flowering earlier. By the time fieldfares and redwings arrive (relatively later) brambles have largely gone removing an important food source. Sycamore, oak and horse chestnut are responding faster to climate change than other species and therefore will have an advantage in the future. Ash, beech and maple seem to be hardly responding at all. We are predicting that the composition of woodlands will change with the more vigorous growers such as sycamore and hawthorn gaining a competitive advantage.

There are available recording forms and guidance notes to cover spring and autumn (Figure 1), or you can visit the website at www.phenology.org.uk. More recorders mean the more robust the data becomes and the map shows more are needed in Scotland. Help would be much appreciated especially if you have records for a number of years. The UK Phenology Network, The Woodland Trust, Autumn Park, Grantham, Lincs NG31 6LL. Telephone: 0800 026 9650. E-mail phenology@woodland-trust.org.uk.

Reference

Guide to Recording Spring and Autumn Events in Nature's Calendar. Woodland Trust, UK Phenology Network.

Figure 1.

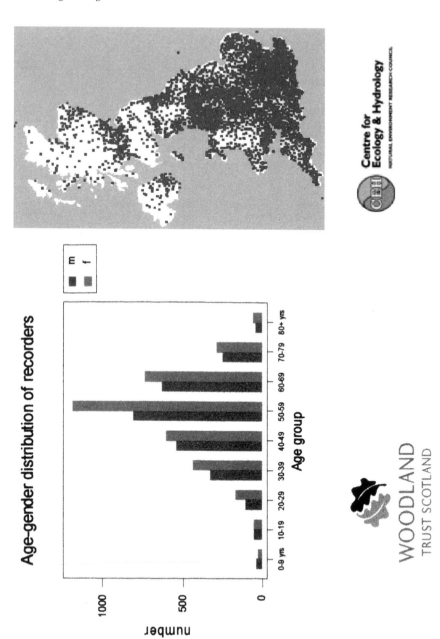

Figure 2.

RECONSTRUCTING THE LAST 1000 YEARS OF SCOTLAND'S CLIMATE
A History of Weather and Climate in the North Atlantic Region

Alastair G. Dawson

Introduction

Much has been written on the history of Scotland. Yet despite, the countless books and papers that trace the footprints of Scottish history to the present, very few documentary accounts have been investigated to extract information on past weather and climate. This is somewhat surprising given our preoccupation with weather and more widespread concerns in respect of 'global warming'. The lack of attention to climate and weather in Scottish history is well illustrated through inspection of virtually every history textbook where there is scarcely any mention of past weather or climate. This is all the more surprising since Scotland has experienced famine on many occasions during the recent historical past – are we thus to assume that all such famines were due to social and political factors – surely not! In the following introductory account, attention is focused on four aspects of the climate and weather of the North Atlantic region that are important in shaping Scotland's climate. Changes in air temperature are considered first. These are followed by a discussion of changes in North Atlantic storminess. Thereafter the role of the North Atlantic ocean in effecting climate change is discussed since the interaction of ocean and atmosphere is so vital an influence on our climate and weather – here we consider firstly the significance of oceanic sea ice and secondly the significance of sea surface temperatures on climate change across the North Atlantic. This brief account, therefore, should serve mark out the starting point of a very complex yet fascinating subject that has an important bearing on the cultural development of Scotland since the time of the first settlers ca. 9,000 years ago.

Chronologies of former air temperature

The first detailed and continuous records of daily weather for Scotland are available from 1867. Prior to this, daily weather records are available for a number of sources but each is restricted to shorter intervals of a few years in length. For example, weather records are available for the Isle of Raasay from 1855 until 1910 (although there are some missing years) while earlier records for Edinburgh are available for the period 1800-1832 from the measurements of Adie. Similarly, a ten year record of air temperatures for the Duke of Buccleuch estate of Branxholm is available for the period 1773-1783. Prior to this record, other accounts are available from diaries, for example those of Turnbull of Alloa (ca. 1690s) and Lamont of Edinburgh (ca. 1650s) although these tend to give monthly temperature summaries. Popular newspapers such as the *Scots Magazine*, first published in the 1740s, contain air temperature data, principally for Edinburgh. The author is not aware of any diary written prior to that of

John Lamont that provides detailed air temperature data for any part of Scotland.

Prior to the 1650s, therefore, it is difficult to reconstruct in any detail, patterns of weather for Scotland. However, there is a very valuable source of proxy weather data for the North Atlantic region contained within the ice of the Greenland ice sheet. Drilling projects undertaken during the 1980s by American and European scientists recovered several thousands of metres of ice. Within the frozen cores are contained various indicators of past weather and climate. For example, measurements of the isotopes of oxygen within the ice give information on past seasonal changes in air temperatures across Greenland. Measurements of concentrations of sodium (Na+) that accumulated through the deposition of sea salt on the ice sheet surface provides a past record of North Atlantic storminess. Similarly, measurements of the chlorine chemistry through each ice core have provided valuable information on periods of time when sea ice was extensive across the Greenland Sea and northern North Atlantic. Measurements of deuterium likewise have provided valuable information on past changes in North Atlantic sea surface temperatures.

One must never assume, however, that past increases and decreases in annual air temperature over Greenland were paralleled by changes of similar sign across Scotland. The existence of a climate 'see-saw' between western Greenland and northern Europe has been known for over 200 years. For example, van Loon and Rogers (1978) quote the missionary Hans Egede Saabye who described in a diary kept during the years AD 1770-78 that *"...In Greenland all winters are severe, yet they are not alike. The Danes have noticed that when the winter in Denmark was severe, as we perceive it, the winter in Greenland in its manner was mild, and conversely"*. Similarly, it has been observed that mild winters in western Greenland frequently correspond with reduced winter temperatures in northern Europe.

The 'see-saw' in winter air temperatures is linked to interannual variability of the Icelandic low pressure cell and the North Atlantic Oscillation (an index based on an analysis of a time series of monthly air pressure differences between Iceland and the Azores). Thus severe winters in northern Europe occur when westerly winds in the North Atlantic region are weak and, there is a blocking ridge of high pressure across the eastern Atlantic and where air temperatures are higher than average across western Greenland. During such periods, northerly flow of air around the east side of the ridge advects cold, polar air from the Arctic across Europe. By contrast, when a cold northerly airstream on the eastern flank of the winter Canadian anticyclone moves over western Greenland, there is marked increase in cyclone frequency across the northern North Atlantic and Scotland experiences its stormiest winters with a dominance of SW winds and an increase in winter air temperatures.

In Scotland, the fragmentary accounts that are available point to a sustained decline in air temperatures during the late 17th century. In particular, the decade of the 1690s is well known for the famines associated with the poor weather and is sometimes referred to as *"...the lean years of dear King William..."*.

The decline in air temperatures enabled the establishment in the 1770s of the Edinburgh Skating Society and it may be the case that such lowered temperatures may have persisted until the close of the 19th century. Remarkably, the derived air temperature time series for central Greenland based on oxygen isotope analysis does not show a clear signal of the Little Ice Age having occurred in central Greenland. Remarkably, two of the coldest winters in central Greenland during the last 2000 years occurred during the winters of AD 1982-83 and 1983-84. During these two winters the average winter air temperatures were respectively –8.6 and -9.0°C below the long term average. By contrast, the same winters were associated in Scotland with average winter air temperatures +0.9 and +2.0°C above the long term average. This simple illustration demonstrates very clearly that it is a big mistake to imagine that past trends in air temperature are of the same sign everywhere – even across such a relatively small area of the earth such as the North Atlantic marked regional differences are very evident.

Changes in North Atlantic storminess

Whereas the oxygen isotope record from central Greenland represents a record of air temperature changes over central and West Greenland, the sodium (Na+) concentrations (sea salt) time series represents a chronology of regional changes in North Atlantic storminess. Plots of the Na+ series for the last 2000 years show a dramatic increase from about 1400-1420. Prior to this period, the winter climate of the North Atlantic was almost unrecognisable from that of today since rarely were there large storms. After 1400-1420, North Atlantic winter storminess became commonplace and this pattern has continued until the present. If one was to select a point in time when the Medieval Warm period (associated with Viking expansion) ended and the Little Ice Age started, it would be at this time. Although distant from Scotland, it should not be forgotten that the last records of Viking settlement in Greenland date to the 1420s. After this time all contact with the Vikings in Greenland was lost. Thus we can envisage the first settlement in Greenland during the 980s as having taken place during a mild episode of the Medieval Warm period during which time winter storminess was at minimum – it would not be inaccurate to suggest that similarly milder winter weather prevailed in Scotland at this time. In Scotland, the dramatic change in winter weather to Little Ice Age conditions marks the time when winters started to become markedly stormier. For example, the accounts by Stevenson of lighthouse construction around the coastline of Scotland provide graphic account of many storms during the late 18th and early 19th century. Other storms left profound marks on Scottish history. For example, a huge storm smashed and scattered the Spanish Armada as far afield as Fair Isle during 1588 while a summer hurricane in 1832 destroyed the haaf fishery fleet off the Shetland Isles.

Changes in sea ice extent

In the 1880s the Royal Geographic Society in London received a report from a Captain Gray of Peterhead on the state of sea ice cover across the northern North Atlantic. The purpose of Captain Gray's report was to draw attention to the huge increase in sea ice cover across the northern North Atlantic that had taken place during the preceding decade. His account expressed concerns that a new ice age may be imminent. Sea ice is normally no more than 1-2 m in thickness. It forms when cold air blows over the northern ocean and is of sufficiently low temperature to cause the surface salt water to freeze. As the sea ice begins to forms, it expels salt into the adjoining waters thus making them dense and causing the saline water to descend to the floor of the ocean. The sinking of this salty water and its return southward flow over the floor of the Atlantic constitutes an important part of global ocean circulation while evaporation of moisture from the northward flowing surface current provides an important part of the supply of heat to northern Europe. The development of sea ice across northern waters is thus an important mechanism in controlling the amount of water that descends to the floor of the Atlantic. It is also important since each summer its melting produced enormous volumes of fresh water that rest upon the ocean surface and only slowly mix with the underlying saline water. Periods of cold climate in Scotland in the past have thus often coincided with periods of increased sea ice cover. In the most extreme case during the last ice age ca. 20,000 years ago, sea ice during winter reached as far south as the latitude of Spain and Portugal. More recently, during the so-called Little Ice Age that affected Scotland between the 15th and 19th centuries it may have reached at its maximum extent as far south as the Shetland Isles. Indeed, according to newspaper reports of the early 1880s, it was possible to climb the hill above Torshavn, the capital of the Faroe Isles and not be able to see the ocean owing to presence of vast areas of sea ice offshore. The occurrence of vast areas of sea ice across the northern North Atlantic may also go some way to account for the arrival in Aberdeen harbour during the 1790s of two Eskimos in a kayak who had most likely been trapped in the extensive areas of sea ice that reached at that time to ca. 50-100 km north of the Shetland Isles. Much has also been written of the importance of sea ice in the demise of the Viking settlements of west Greenland during the early 15th century through its role in restricting the passage of sea vessels between Scandinavia, Iceland and Greenland.

Analysis of Greenland ice core chemistry as well as the Viking sagas has also helped to provide a remarkable record of past changes in sea ice extent. It appears that a prolonged period of reduced sea ice cover occurred between ca.AD 200 and 1400 with two possible reversals during the early 8th century and the late 10th century. For the most part, therefore, Viking expansion in Scotland took place during benign climatic conditions during which seafaring was much easier than it later became from the 15th century onwards. According to the Viking Sagas, sea ice first appeared around Iceland during the 1270s. After ca. AD 1420 there appears to have been a stepwise increase in sea ice extent that culminated as late as the 1880s.

The presence or absence of sea ice cannot be underestimated in its importance to climate changes across the North Atlantic (and hence also Scotland). Sea ice starts to form during December and reaches its maximum extent during May/June. Thus, during years when sea ice was very extensive, its presence may have played an important role in determining the nature of summer weather across Scotland. During such times, the North Atlantic storm track was displaced farther south than normal and, under such circumstances, 'big' sea ice years were often accompanied by summer storminess. During the 19th century some of these storms took fishermen by surprise and led to loss of life, particularly in the Shetland fisheries but also notably in the case of the Eyemouth tragedy of 1881.

Changes in North Atlantic sea surface temperature

Greenland ice core data has also been used to derive annual records of past North Atlantic sea surface temperatures through the application of deuterium excess analysis. To date , this analysis has been used to reconstruct seasonal sea surface temperature changes for the last ca. 700 years. The patterns of change that have been calculated point to particular time intervals during which major and rapid changes in ocean circulation have taken place and almost certainly linked to past changes in ocean circulation. One of these changes took place between ca. 1400-1420 coincident with the sharp increase in N Atlantic storminess. During these two decades, North Atlantic ocean temperatures did not rise appreciably during summer nor did they fall during winter. The most dramatic changes, however, took place between ca. 1315-1335. During this time there was an exceptional period of ocean warmth (warmer during both during summer and winter for about 5 years) that was followed by a switch to about 5 years of ocean cooling (cooler during both during summer and winter). This pattern of change was repeated again between 1325-1335. Historical accounts of past weather show that the episodes of ocean warming were associated with exceptional rainfall (winter and summer) across the UK while the episodes of cooling were associated with drought. It remains for historians to evaluate the degree to which these remarkable changes in climate played a part in post-Bannockburn Scotland, regarded by many as a time of dearth and famine.

Summary

Information on past weather and climate for Scotland is available in most library archives. Most of this information has never been examined in any detail. Many historical diaries also contain valuable information on past weather yet few diaries have been read carefully in order to extract meteorological and climatological data. Similarly, indexed newspapers contain valuable weather records in their pages. At present these various sources of weather data are being painstakingly examined for the first time in order to piece together a chronology of past climate. The task is an onerous one but one that yields fascinating insights into the past weather events that posed such tremendous challenges to our ancestors.

Further Reading

Barlow, L.K., White, J.W.C., Barry, R.G., Rogers, J.C. and Grootes, P.M. 1993: The North Atlantic Oscillation signature in deuterium and deuterium excess signals in the Greenland Ice Sheet Project 2 ice core, 1840-1970. *Geophysical Research Letters* 20(24), 2901-2904.

Bradley, R.S. and Jones, P.D. 1991: *Climate since 1500 AD*. London: Methuen Press.

Dawson, A.G., Hickey, K., Holt, T., Elliott, L., Dawson, S., Foster, I.D.L., Wadhams, P., Jonsdottir, I., Wilkinson, J., McKenna, J., Davis, N.R. and Smith, D.E. 2002: Complex North Atlantic Oscillation (NAO) index signal of historic North Atlantic storm track changes. *The Holocene* 12(3), 363-370.

Dawson, A.G., Elliott, L., Mayewski, P., Lockett, P., Noone, S., Hickey, K., Holt, T., Wadhams, P. and I. Foster 2003 Late Holocene North Atlantic climate 'seesaws', storminess changes and Greenland ice sheet (GISP2) palaeoclimates. *The Holocene* 13, 381-392.

Meeker, L.D. and Mayewski, P.A. 2002: A 1400 year long record of atmospheric circulation over the North Atlantic and Asia. *The Holocene* 12(3), 257-266.

Van Loon, H. and Rogers, J.C. 1978: The see-saw in winter temperatures between Greenland and Northern Europe. Part I: general description. *Monthly Weather Review* 106, 296-310.

DETECTING CHANGES IN CLIMATE AT A LOCAL LEVEL

John Harrison

The broad picture of climatic change

Changeability is a major characteristic of the Scottish climate, but it is the presence of detectable long-term changes throughout the 20th century and the prospect of further changes through the 21st that are currently major issues. The climatic record for Scotland is relatively sparse but from what is available it has been possible to identify significant trends when information from a number of locations is aggregated. The most marked changes have been since the 1970s (Table 1a). Available climatic models suggest that many of these changes are part of an ongoing trend that is driven primarily by the enhancement of the Greenhouse Effect (Table 1b). Taking aside the deficiencies of climatic data, and the limitations of the climatic models the key question to address is how such large scale changes will be manifested at a local level. Will everywhere in Scotland experience the same changes, and what does the future hold for the weather in, for example, Stirling, Falkirk, Callander, or Aberfoyle?

Problems begin when attempts are made to scale down from a national and regional level to a local level. The simple answers to the above questions are that it is certain that there will be considerable spatial variation in changes in climate, and that climatologists are not sure what changes will occur for every location in Scotland. If attempting to predict climatic change at a local, rather than global or national level, there are two fundamental problems to be overcome, these being the (a) the need to scale down the currently available climatic models and (b) the ever present, and largely unquantifiable, local factors.

Scaling down Climatic Models

The models that are used to predict climate have until recently been capable of making predictions at only the broadest scale, just two large grid squares covering the whole of Scotland in the 1998 predictions from the Hadley Centre. While modelling is improving and the scale in recent models has come down to 50 km in Regional Climate Models, change at a local level requires predictions at 1 km scale or better. At this spatial resolution the climatic processes become complex. There are a number of major climatic controls at this scale such as the effects of open water (coasts and lakes), topography (altitude, aspect, slope, exposure), and land use (urban areas and vegetation/crops for example).

While climatologists have a reasonable understanding of how these effects operate, surfaces are too complex to model and models are also not universal. Brunsdon *et al.* (2001), for example, found that the effects of altitude on rainfall in the United Kingdom varies considerably from one location to another.

One alternative is to use a combination of climatic analogues linked to Digital Elevation Modelling in a Geographic Information System (GIS). Such a technique has been used to estimate how snow cover may change in Scotland (Harrison, *et al.* 2001). Winters were chosen from the existing climate record to match as closely as possible the temperature and precipitation predictions relating to the different climatic scenarios. Spatial patterns of the total number of winter days with snow lying were then produced for each winter using crude geographical models which related days with snow lying to latitude, longitude and altitude. The resulting maps at 1 km resolution provided a measure of prediction at a local scale but the precision is spurious and all that can be gained from such an exercise is a broad indication of possible changes in the future.

It has been a common assumption that suitable climatic data will exist for any location and that climatic trends can be readily detected and cross-checked against climatic prediction. This is far from being the case. Spatial coverage by climate stations in Scotland is poor. Many are located on the coasts while there are virtually none in the mountains. Climate stations mostly have a limited lifespan, operating for a few years only. Consequently there are relatively few from which the longer term trends of change can be determined. Little is still known about how the climate is changing in, for example, mountain and hill areas, which are crucial as these are marginal environments for many species of plants and animals.

The conclusion must be that it is difficult to scale down from current climatic models, which will remain the case for some considerable time to come. However, it is reasonable to conclude that what is predicted at a regional or national level may be manifest in a different set of changes at a particular locality. One question that can be answered for the Stirling area is, given the nature of changes in the general nature of climate over Scotland, do local climatic records indicate similar changes or are effects damped or magnified by local conditions?

Local climatic trends

The Stirling University Climate Station, inappropriately named Parkhead, is one of the few climatological stations in the Stirling area with any length of record. The station was established in 1970 by the Department of Biology and data were first published by the Meteorological Office in 1971. The station remains open, so there was an uninterrupted 32 year record by the end of 2002. When it was first established there were stations at Batterflats in Stirling and at Earl's Hill, but these closed in 1982 and 1980 respectively. The only local addition in recent years has been the station at Stirling Sewage Works which was opened in 1984.

The site at Parkhead is far from ideal. It is very sheltered from between NW and NE and there has been one change of site in 1995 when the station was moved a little over 100 m to its current location (Harrison, 2001). Both old and new stations were run simultaneously for nine months to make sure that records would be homogeneous. There was little obvious change in air temperature and rainfall resulting from the change of site. The question is whether the Parkhead data can provide any insight into trends in the local climate in the Stirling area.

Rainfall

The national climatic trends and models indicate a tendency towards wetter winter months over Scotland, particularly in the west of the country. Winter (December/January/February) rainfall totals for Parkhead were analysed and over 30 years there was a statistically significant increase in winter rainfall (Figure 1). The equation generated for the straight line leads to an inferred 47 % increase in winter rainfall. If this is extrapolated forward to 2080 the inference is that rainfall will be almost doubled, which is well in excess of the 20 % predicted by climate models (Hume and Jenkins, 1998) under worse-case scenarios, but it is likely that percentage changes will be higher towards the west and lower towards the east of the country.

Summer Temperature

Models and trends suggest we should expect a warming of the summer months. Although not statistically significant, the trend of summer maximum temperature (June-September) suggests an increase of 0.8°C over 30 years (Figure 2). The changes in the summer temperature have been driven most strongly by a statistically significant increase in September temperatures. Extrapolating trends to 2080 implies that summer days will become a litte over 2.0°C warmer on average. This is consistent with predictions for Scotland (Hulme and Jenkins, 1998).

Growing Season

Minimum temperatures are most often interpreted in terms of frost occurrence. The time elapsed between the last air frost in spring and the air first frost of autumn marks the length of the frost-free season. Although there is not a statistically significant trend in season length, the data appears to suggest an increase in the length of the growing season of 28 days, which tends to match with people's own experiences and with monitored changes in key habitats (Figure 3). An analysis of the dates of the last and first frosts, indicates that there has been a marginally greater extension of the season at the autumn end, this having been extended by more than a fortnight.

Heating within buildings

It is reasonable to suppose that if winter temperatures are improving then less heat will be required to maintain internal temperatures within the University buildings. Daily maximum and minimum temperatures were converted into heating day-degrees below 15.5°C for the entire Parkhead record and the values accumulated from the start of a nominal academic year on October 1st. The number of days elapsed before totals of 500, 1000 and 1500 day-degrees were reached were derived. If winters are getting warmer the number of days should increase through time. Of these the number of days to reach 1500 day-degrees showed a significant increase. In the early 1970s the total was reached on average in the third week of February whereas in 2002 it falls in the first week of March. (Figure 4.) Breaking this down into components reveals a significant increase in the time interval between reaching 1000 and 1500 units which suggests a significant warming between approximately the middle of December and mid-late February which is consistent with the earlier start to the thermal growing season.

Conclusion

Despite reservations about its quality, the local climatic data from Parkhead would appear to be broadly consistent with what has been happening nationally. In this case, Stirling should expect a further lengthening of the frost-free season, warmer summers, wetter and milder winters, and heating bills should decrease.

References

Brunsdon, C., McClatchey, J. and Unwin D.J. (2001). Spatial variations in the Average Rainfall – Altitude relationship in Great Britain: An approach using geographically weighted regression *International Journal of Climatology* 21 (4) 455-466.

Harrison, S.J. (2001). Thirty years of weather observations at Parkhead. Forth *Naturalist and Historian* 24, 15-22.

Harrison, S.J. and Kirkpatrick, A.H. (2001). *Climatic change and its potential implications for environments in Scotland*. In. *Earth Science and the Natural Heritage*. (ed. J.E. Gordon and K.F. Leys) pp296-305. Edinburgh: The Stationery Office.

Harrison, S.J., Winterbottom, S.J. and Johnson R.C. (2001). Climatic Change and Changing Snowfall Patterns in Scotland *Scottish Executive Central Research Unit Environment Group Research Finding 14*. Edinburgh: The Stationery Office.

Hulme, M. and Jenkins, G.J. (1998). Climate change scenarios for the UK: scientific report. *UKCIP Technical Report No. 1* Climate Research Unit, Norwich 80pp.

TABLE 1a
Recent Changes in the Scottish Climate since the early 1970s
(from Harrison and Kirkpatrick, 2001).

Hours of Bright Sunshine
- An imperfect measure of insolation, but indications are of a significant decrease during the winter months, particularly in the west.
- Some weak evidence of an increase in the east during winter and over the whole of Scotland during the summer and autumn.

Air Temperature
- *Maximum temperatures:* Changes have been relatively small but there is some evidence of increases of up to 0.3°C. The most significant long-term upward trend has been in spring.
- *Minimum temperatures:* Evidence of increases >0.5°C during the late winter months. The most significant upward trend has been in spring and early summer.

Precipitation
- *Rainfall:* Increased totals in all seasons but only significant during the winter months, most notably in the North and West.
- *Snowfall:* Some evidence of a downward trend in the during of winter days with snow lying.

Airflow
- Very difficult to identify any trend in wind speed due to the nature of the available data. Indications are that gales have increased in frequency and severity. The decade 1988-1997 has seen the highest frequency of gales since the late 19th Century.

TABLE 1b
Potential changes of climate in Scotland during the 21st Century according to current collective wisdom.

Increase in near-surface air temperature

Decrease in the intensity of very cold spells in winter

Marked decrease in the frequency of frosts

Increase in annual rainfall

Marked reduction in snowfall and days with snow lying

Convective shower precipitation more frequent

Decrease in the number of rainy days
but an increase in the amount falling on each day

Possible increase in river flood frequency

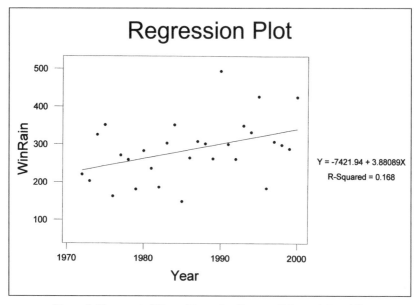

Figure 1. Changes in Winter (December, January, February) Rainfall.

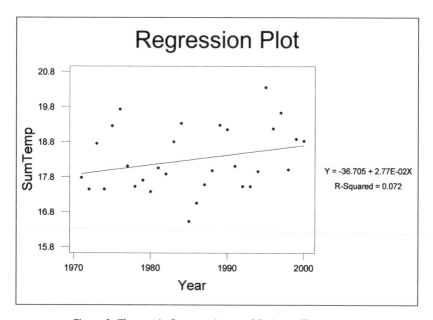

Figure 2. Changes in Summer Average Maximum Temperature
(June, July, August, September).

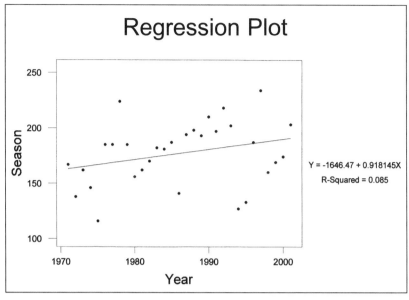

Figure 3. Changes in the length of the frost-free (0.0°C) season
(days elapsed between the last air frost in spring and the first in autumn).

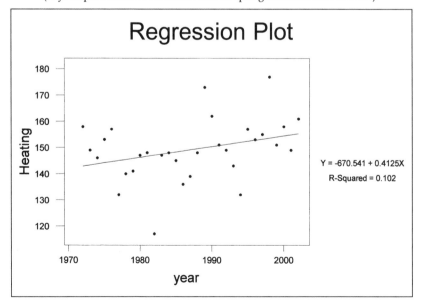

Figure 4. Changes in the number of days elapsed from October 1st to
accumulate 1500 heating days degrees below 15.5°C.

BOOK REVIEWS

People and Woods in Scotland: a History. Ed. T. C. Smout. 2003. Edinburgh University Press. 26opp. ISBN 0 7486 1701 9. £14.99.

From 11,500 years ago when the ice melted and trees returned bringing the birds and mammals, and soon after the first hunter-gathering humans, the book charts and explains Scotland's great loss of trees over the following millennia, the 20th century revival of forests and woodlands, and ends in examining the changes now underway.

With distinguished authors the chapters cover – prehistory to 1000BC, coming of iron to 500AD, medieval to 1600, using the woods to 1850 the 'planters' 1650 to 1900, 20th century take off, ecological impact of using, and the future. Lastly are 20pp of data on species, references, readings, index commissioned by the Forestry Commission this is a key authoritative well produced and illustrated work.

Scottish Association of Geography Teachers Journal, vol 31 2002. Reading the Landscape. 120pp.

Papers of the seminar at Stirling University June 2002 – incl. cultural geographies, landscape and literature, soils approach…

Early Prehistory of Scotland. Eds. T. Pollard and A. Morrison. Edinburgh University Press. 200pp. ISBN 0 7486 0677 7. Not priced.

The Birdwatcher's Yearbook and Diary. 2004. Pubn 29 Oct. Buckingham Press. £15.

Where to Watch Birds in Scotland. Miles Madders and Julia Welstead. 4th edn. 300pp. A. & C. Black. £14.99.

Information set out by areas – 5pp on Central Scotland, Forth Estuary…

Scottish Birds. Valarie Thom. Collins. 256pp. ISBN 0 00 219983 1. £9.99.

Well presented data on habitats and their birds under headings – garden, farmland, woodland, freshwater, heath and hill, coast, by the former president of SOC.

Footpaths of Scotland. Lomond Books. 64pp. £3.

"An illustrated guide to our 30 most beautiful walks" – includes Loch Ard Forest from Aberfoyle.

The Story of Hillwalking. Ralph Storer. Luath Press. 160pp. ISBN 0 946487 28 6. £7.50.

The Waste Crisis: landfills, incinerators, and the search for a sustainable future. Hans Tammenmagi. OUP. 280pp. ISBN 0 19 512898 2.

While its purpose is an overview of waste management in N. America, its comprehensive treatment of this huge and complex subject marks it as a good source suitable for a wide readership, general and academic, for both study and reference. It encourages readers to constantly challenge commonly held views and practices about garbage/waste, and to seek new and better ways of dealing with it.

CLACKMANNANSHIRE BREEDING BIRD ATLAS

Andre E. Thiel

Introduction

A great deal is known about the distribution of breeding birds on a national scale through schemes such as the Common Bird Census (CBC), the Breeding Bird Survey (BBS) as well as through the national breeding atlases carried out in the 1970s (Sharrock, 1976) and late 1980s (Gibbons *et al.*, 1993). The CBC and BBS surveys are of representative sets of sample areas. However in Clackmannanshire there are no CBC localities and only two 1 km BBS squares, both in the upland Ochils. The national atlases, by necessity, took place at a fairly large scale (10 km², of which there are only two in Clackmannanshire) with very little data having been contributed from the county.

Detailed studies at the local level (*e.g.* Henty, 1977) can yield very interesting results but focus on particular species or small, well-defined localities. For the local (and visiting) birdwatcher, what is arguably of highest interest is a picture of the avifauna at the intermediate, regional level.

In recent years, the Scottish Ornithologists' Club (SOC) has been encouraging the production of regional atlases to yield data on regional trends, which often reveal added detail that is not necessarily evident in national statistics. For instance, the current spread of nuthatch from the Borders into Central Scotland or the local extinction of corn bunting is not evident in national trend data. In Scotland regional atlas projects have been completed in North-east Scotland (Buckland *et al.*, 1990) and, more recently, in South-east Scotland (Murray *et al.*, 1998), while atlas work is in progress in Clyde and nearing completion in Fife.

The breeding birds of Clackmannanshire

Relatively little is known about the current breeding status of birds in Clackmannanshire. Although the county is covered by *The Check List of the Birds of Central Scotland* (Henty & Brackenridge, 1992), most of the information contained in that list relates to the much larger neighbouring county of Stirlingshire. The bird reports for the Forth area (1974-2002), published in the *Forth Naturalist and Historian*, do distinguish between the three counties but even they contain little information on the breeding status of most common birds.

In February 2002, two local ornithologists – the author and Neil Bielby – got together and set up a steering group comprising representatives from the SOC, the British Trust for Ornithology (BTO), the local bird recorder, etc. to carry out a breeding bird atlas for the Clackmannanshire local authority area. With 160 km², Clackmannanshire is the smallest local authority area in mainland Britain. This notwithstanding, it is a region of great habitat diversity, rising from the inner estuary of the Forth (4 m asl.) to the peaks of the Ochils (721 m asl.) – a real Scotland in miniature. This, in turn, gives rise to a large diversity of breeding niches for many bird species.

The small size of the county has the advantage that it is possible to study bird breeding behaviour at a much finer scale – the 1 x 1 km square – compared to the tetrad level (2 x 2 km square) used by most other regional atlases. In addition, the Clackmannanshire Breeding Bird Atlas (CBBA) is breaking new ground by linking breeding distribution to detailed and the most up-to-date habitat distribution data available.

Objectives & methodology

The objectives of the Atlas are fourfold:

* *To map the distribution of all bird species occurring in Clackmannanshire*

There are a total of 198 1 x1 km squares in Clackmannanshire (130 full and 68 partial squares). Based on the interest generated, it is thought that fieldwork can be completed within 5 years to be followed by one year for analysing and editing the data. This coincides with the start of the next national breeding atlas, thereby providing a useful baseline for comparisons.

The methodology used is based on the standard international methodology used by most atlases in the UK. It records birds in four categories (observed only, possibly breeding, probably breeding and definitely breeding), depending on their behaviour (*e.g.* inactive, singing, displaying, carrying food) or other features (*e.g.* nest containing eggs).

Two recording sheets are used: a main sheet allocated for specific squares where several visits per square are required and a supplementary sheet for recording incidental data anywhere in the county. Additional data (*e.g.* data submitted to the bird recorder) will also be added to the database where applicable.

* *To obtain abundance data for common species*

In a second stage of the project, the atlas will use a BBS-type methodology in a representative sample of localities for each of the major habitat types to obtain abundance data for those species which are sufficiently common to allow statistically robust extrapolations to be made for the entire county.

* *To link distribution and abundance to habitat distribution*

The atlas will use the Phase 1 survey of Clackmannanshire (Todd & Brackenridge, 1995) and the 1999 aerial photo interpretation data for areas not covered by the former (Thiel & Lindsay, 1999) as a baseline of habitat distribution. Surveyors are issued habitat maps for their respective squares and asked to mark any deviations at the time of survey so as to obtain the most up-to-date habitat distribution data. This will also allow a measure of the rate of habitat change during the course of the project for those squares that are revisited in successive years.

- *To link in with the UK Biodiversity Action Plan (UK BAP) and the Clackmannanshire Local Biodiversity Action Plan (LBAP)*

Very little information is available on BAP priority species at the local level, as reflected by actions in most of the LBAP Species Action Plans to collect such data. The atlas will not only provide these data at the 1 km² level but also link them to habitat use, through surveyors mapping the location of all priority species on the habitat maps provided to them. In this way the data generated through the project can be used for direct conservation action at the local level.

Results from the 2002 & 2003 breeding seasons

Despite the very wet weather of 2002, results were most encouraging. Data were returned from 86 squares (43 % of all 1 x 1 km squares). Fifty-three (27 %) of these were covered in detail, the rest having incidental data collected for them. Two fifths (40 %) of the squares covered in detail were in the less accessible upland Ochils.

A total of 103 species were recorded in the first year. Of these, 47 species (46 %) were confirmed as breeding. Highlights included:
– the first confirmed breeding record for red grouse since 1978
– the first confirmed breeding record for raven since 1987
– only the second confirmed breeding records for ringed plover and tree sparrow in Clackmannanshire
– confirmed breeding record for kingfisher

In addition, eight of the nine UK Biodiversity Action Plan priority species known to occur in Clackmannanshire were recorded and breeding was confirmed for four of these.

The most commonly recorded species during the 2002 season was carrion crow, which was recorded in 41 squares out of 86 (48 %) and proven to be breeding in seven of these. The next most common species were blackbird (recorded in 34 squares, proven breeding in 15 squares), wren (34, 5) and chaffinch (34, 2). Close behind were woodpigeon (32, 4), blue tit (31, 10), willow warbler (30, 2), robin (28, 11), mallard (28, 8) and skylark (28, 0). The most widespread breeding species was Starling, which was confirmed breeding in 18 of the 24 squares it was recorded in. Other species for which evidence of breeding was obtained include, amongst others, great crested grebe (3, 1), shelduck (4, 1), grey wagtail (8, 2), dipper (10, 1), spotted flycatcher (1, 1), wheatear (7, 1), whitethroat (19, 1), long-tailed tit (14, 4), linnet (15, 2) and yellowhammer (21, 1).

At the start of the 2003 season, another 25 % of the 1 km squares had been allocated for survey and it is estimated that by the end of the season about 40 % of all squares will have been covered in detail, which is right on target, with incidental records collected for many more squares.

At the time of writing, the first results were just being returned to the organisers. Data from only a handful of squares are very encouraging. New species added to the list include little egret, egyptian goose (escapee), shoveler, pochard, ruddy duck, dunlin, ruff, woodcock, black-tailed godwit, greenshank, green sandpiper, long-eared owl, barn owl, tree pipit and redpoll.

While most of these refer to non-breeding records, some are of interest in their own right. The little egret record, for instance, is the first ever record of this species in Clackmannanshire. The long-eared owl record refers to a brood, while the barn owl record is only the third record of that species since 1978 and the first breeding record since systematic recording began in 1974.

A more detailed synopsis will be possible once all results from the 2003 have been returned and analysed.

How you can get involved

Whether you live in Clackmannanshire, pass through the county on a regular basis or are a visitor the area, you can take part in the scientific study of the distribution of breeding birds in Clackmannanshire.

To contribute incidental data, you don't have to be an accomplished ornithologist; we are just as interested in the birds breeding in your garden as those seen on a walk through the countryside. If you are interested in getting more heavily involved and can spare the time to visit an area near you on a few occasions between April and July, you can take on a full square. In that case, you need to be able to identify birds by sight and, ideally, by sound as well.

Either way, further details and recording forms for the 2004 season are available from the local organiser, Neil Bielby (tel. 01786-823 830).

Acknowledgements

The atlas fieldwork would not have been possible without the assistance of the many volunteer surveyors who have taken part. The author is most grateful to all who took part in 2002 and 2003. Thanks are also due to the SOC for financial assistance towards the running costs of the atlas.

References

Buckland, S.T., Bell, M.V. and Picozzi, N. (1990) *The Birds of North-east Scotland*. North-east Scotland Bird Club: Aberdeen.

Gibbons, D.W., Reid, J.B. and Chapman, R.A. (1993) *The New Atlas of Breeding Birds in Britain and Ireland: 1988-1991*. T.&A.D. Poyser: London.

Henty, C.J. (1977) The roost-flights of Whooper Swans in the Devon Valley (Central Scotland). *Forth Naturalist and Historian*, 2, 31-35.

Henty, C.J. and Brackenridge, W.R. (1992) Check List of the Birds of Central Scotland. *Forth Naturalist and Historian*, 15, 19-26.

Murray, R.D., Holling, M., Dott, H.E. and Vandome, P. (1998) *The Breeding Birds of South-east Scotland. The Tetrad Atlas 1988-1994*. The Scottish Ornithologists' Club: Edinburgh.

Sharrock, J.T.R. (1976) *The Atlas of Breeding Birds in Britain and Ireland*. T.&A.D. Poyser: London.

Thiel, A.E. and Lindsay, H. (1999) *Clackmannanshire Local Biodiversity Action Plan Habitat Audit. Technical Report*. Report to Clackmannanshire Council, Alloa.

Todd, T. and Brackenridge, W.R. (1995) *Clackmannan District Habitat Contexting Survey*. Report to Scottish Natural Heritage and Central Region Council, Stirling.

FORTH AREA BIRD REPORT 2002

C.J. Henty and A.E. Thiel

This report is compiled from a larger archive of records submitted to the local recorder under the national scheme organised by the Scottish Ornithologists' Club.This has been a bumper year for our first records of rare species – at Skinflats Little Egrets appeared in both spring and autumn whilst a Caspian Tern made a brief but spectacular sight in July; a Rosy Starling, part of a widespread influx, came twice to a garden in Gartmore but never coincided with local birding experts. The spring was marked by a brief but remarkable passage of Black-tailed Godwits, mainly at Skinflats but flocks also seen on marshes in our highland area. In Glen Dochart another apparently unmated Common Rosefinch sang in midsummer and Magpies were noted well out of the usual range.

Red Kites continue to do fairly well, but persistent rain in late spring led to many failures in breeding Peregrines and Ospreys. An industrial sites survey at a gravel working in the Teith valley led to the discovery of a thriving colony of Black-headed and Common Gulls. Amongst winter visitors the regular drake Smew at L.Dochart stayed into February but failed to appear in autumn, and there continue to be surprisingly large numbers of Goldeneye on the lower Devon. On the estuary the largest flock of Great Crested Grebes was at Blackness and an unusual influx of divers occured in November, whilst devotees of rubbish dumps found Glaucous and Iceland Gulls. There are more reports of ringed Mute Swans and their movements through central Scotland. A Greenshank wintered at Skinflats and there are signs that Green Sandpipers are wintering inland on small rivers throughout the region. No large autumn influx of the scarcer waders occurred and the passage of Scandinavian thrushes was only modest.

Most months in 2002 were milder and wetter than average (rainfall at Dunblane 26 % up) and only two days had snowfall. Summer was unusually wet to be followed by an Indian Summer in late September and then frequent easterly winds. January started with the coldest day of the year on the 2nd (–9.6 at Dunblane) but overall was the warmest for eight years with heavy rain throughout the last two weeks. February also was slightly milder and wetter than the norm with rain on twenty five days and one snowfall on the 22nd. The first three weeks of March were very wet, plus one brief snowfall on the 10th, but it then became dry and sunny for the end of the month. Although April started with a torrential thunderstorm on the 3rd there followed a dry week and, although the rest of the month was unsettled with variable temperature, the month was overall warmer and slightly dryer than average. The first half of May showed some dry and sunny days but there was then rain on every day to give a total 77 % up on the norm and the wet weather continued through June – overall rainfall up 100 %. July gave no respite, rain on 24 days with heavy thundery rain on the 12th and 30th to make it the wettest spring or summer month in eight years. August was average in temperature and rainfall with eleven sunny days and the warmest day of the year (25.4°C) on the 4th. Although early September was mainly unsettled, with thunderstorms on the 8th and 9th, it then became dry and warm with only 2.3 mm of rain thereafter. October started dry and warm but there was some heavy rain and eight days of frost in the last three weeks to end up slightly wetter and colder than usual. Easterly winds persisted through November, though there was only one frost and rain occurred on twenty seven days. December continued the easterly airstream pattern but although it was much dryer and warmer than the norm (only six frosts) it remained persistently dull with sun being seen only on seven days.

Annual Bird Reports depend entirely on contributions from the local birdwatching community, as far as possible these are acknowledged with initials as well as the full name list in the introduction. Eighty-three contributors appear this year, there is more use of computer databases, sent by email or floppy disc, but it is important that these are in the same format as the main database; a copy of this can be got from CJH. The supply of BTO record cards has dried up but ordinary file cards (6x4 in) are good alternatives if the same basic information is written in.

The sparse information available about common breeding species is greatly improved by the resumption of the Breeding Birds Survey after last year's outbreak of foot and mouth disease. For less common species we can sometimes mention data in terms of the numbers of pairs or apparently occupied territories for particular locations. The organisers for both the estuary and the inland waters parts of the national wildfowl counts (WEBS) have made available the results for this report. These often contribute to the species accounts and there is also a separate summary for inland waters which concentrates on localities.

Several observers send in a list largely or entirely for their home locality, much of this information is not appropriate for these annual reports but it is valuable to have on record and we are keeping them in a special file. At the moment there are fifteen such lists referring to the whole district from Falkirk to Killin.

For many species the records sent in are very unrepresentative of their general distribution, this applies particularly to very common species or to those that are secretive or breed in inaccessable places. Readers can consult the the Check List published in the Forth Naturalist and Historian vol 15, but in addition I have in this report put, after the species name, a coded summary of general distribution – which often apparently contradicts the detailed records that are published for the year.

B - Breeding status, widespread (in more than five 10 km squares)
b   "   "   , local, scarce (in fewer than five 10 km squares)
W - Winter status, widespread or often in groups of more than ten.
w -   "   "   , local, scarce (local and usually fewer than ten in a group)
P - Passage (used when species is usually absent in winter, P or p used for

widespread or local as in winter status)

S or s - a few species are present in summer but do not normally breed.

Thus BW would be appropriate for Robin, B for Swallow, p for Ruff and SW for Cormorant. No status letter is used if a species occurs less than every other year.

An asterix (*) in front of the species name means that all records received have been quoted.

The SOC has pressed for a more systematic vetting of records of species that are unusual locally, this area now has an informal panel of five – C. Henty (Recorder), A. Smith, D. Orr-Ewing, A. Blair and D. Thorogood. The judging of national UK or Scottish rarities continues as before, but we have produced for the upper Forth a list of species that are scarce locally and where the records need to be supported by either a full description or sufficient evidence to remove any reasonable doubt. Any species which is a vagrant to the area, and most of those which are asterisked in this report, will come into this category. Observers should be aware that aberrant individuals of common species of birds appear quite regularly and these sometimes resemble rarities. There is also the problem of escaped cage birds and of hybridisation, a particular problem in captive wildfowl which may then appear in natural situations.

The following abbreviations have been used : AoT - apparently occupied territory, BoA - Bridge of Allan, c/n - clutch of n eggs, BBS - Breeding Bird Survey, CBC- Common Bird Census, CP - Country Park, F - Female, G – Glen, GP - gravel pit, J - juvenile, L. - Loch, NR - Nature Reserve, M - Male, ON - on nest, Res - Reservoir, SP - summer plumage, WEBS – Wetland Bird Survey, Y - young.

The area covered by the report comprises the council areas of Falkirk and Clackmannan together with Stirling, excluding Loch Lomondside and other parts of the Clyde drainage basin. Please note that we do not include the Endrick water, *i.e.* Fintry and Balfron. Records from Carron Valley Reservoir are published here but it is proposed that Clyde should cover all the forest south of the reservoir.

This report has been compiled from records submitted by:

J.H. Allan, D. Anderson, M. Anderson, M.V. Bell, N. Bielby, Birdline Scotland, A. Blair, R.A. Broad, G. J Brock, D.M. Bryant, R. Bullman, D.J. Cameron, H. Cameron, B. Caving, R. Chapman, D.&A. Christie, L. Corbett, R.&A. Daly, R.J. Dawson, P. Dearing, A. Downie, A. Duncombe, D. Egerton, K. Egerton, C.J. Henty, D. Jones, R. Jones, M. Kobs, G.&E. Leisk, D.&M. Mason, J. Mitchell, J. Nimmo, D. Orr-Ewing, G. Owens, D. Pickett, R. K. Pollock, D. Rees, H. Robb, P.W. Sandeman, A. Smith, C. Smout, P. Stirling-Aird, D. Thorogood, A. Thiel, J. Wheeler, J.N. Willett, K. Wilkinson.

Thanks are due to Dr M.V. Bell for compiling the sections on geese, to J. Mitchell for forwarding notes on Carron Valley, to D. Orr-Ewing for RSPB data on Red Kites and Ospreys, to P. Stirling-Aird for data from the Raptor Study

Group, to Prof. D.M. Bryant for the results of the estuary WEBS data, and to N. Bielby for meterological data from Dunblane. E. Cameron transcribed records onto the database.

WEBS contributors to these data, additional to report list were: A. Ayre, B. Barker, S. Easthaugh, M. Ferguson, M. Hardy, I. Henderson, A. Moody, R. Osborn, E.&J. Payne, S. Ramsay, D. Shenton, H. Weir, A. Wallace, M. White, A. Watterson, A. Wilson.

RESULTS OF THE BBS SURVEYS FOR CENTRAL REGION.
(Based on a comprehensive summary by NB).

These surveys were resumed in 2002 after the 2001 programme had to be cancelled due to the foot and mouth outbreak. These data are in terms of the frequency of occurence of a species along linear transects in several habitat types. In 2002, 26 1x1 km squares were surveyed, three less than 2000. Each square is usually visited twice in spring/summer, a total of 2 km on a set route is walked per visit and all birds noted in 200 m sections; a standardised habitat survey is done on another visit. In the main report we have presented selected results, calculated as birds per ten kilometres of habitat, for the major habitats where it is likely that the birds are breeding locally; overall figures for comparing across years are calculated for the total transect length for the whole area. For species that are scarce – say, one or less per 10 km – results may vary erratically from year to year.

Each square (sometimes half squares) and the birds noted in it have been attributed to one of four major habitats – Mountain and moorland (=moor), Conifers (woodland + wood/moorland edge), Farmland, and Urban/suburban. Broadleaved woodland occurs mainly as copses in farmland whilst conifer woodland includes both young plantations and mature woods, thus "Conifers" figures may include species of scrub and moorland edge which are not found in mature plantations. Also, some urban squares may include bushy areas on the fringe of towns.

An average of 25 species was recorded per square but with great variation from five on high moorland to 39 on mixed farmland, numbers of individuals also varied widely from 48 to 490, median 219. The commonest species per habitat were: Moor – Meadow Pipit, Conifer – Willow Warbler, Farmland – Rook, Sub/Urban – Starling. Species showing marked increases (40 % or greater over 2000) included Blackcap, Coal Tit, Blue Tit, Great Tit, Spotted Flycatcher, Siskin and Reed Bunting. Cuckoo,Whinchat and Bullfinch are now well below their long term means.

2002 contributors were: M.A., N.B., B. Barker, R. Bullman, J. Calladine, D.A.C., D.J.C., P. Carter, R.C., A. Downie, R.D., D.E., M. Ferguson, J. Grainger, J.N., D.J., M.K., G.E.L., A. Moody, M.D.M., D.O.E., R. Osborn, D.P., E.&J. Payne, S. Ramsay, A.T., M.T., D. Redwood, S. Sankey, D. Shenton, C. Wernham, J.W., J.N.W.

WILDFOWL REPORT 2001-2002

This report concerns the inland waters part of this area's Wetland Bird Survey (WEBS) organised by NB and is a condensed version of a fuller report by him.

WEBS is a monthly waterfowl census under the auspices of the British Trust for Ornithology (BTO) and the Wildfowl & Wetlands Trust (WWT), it runs from September to March inclusive. For this report 'wildfowl' includes divers, grebes, cormorants, herons, swans, geese (excluding Pink-footed and Greylag for which the WWT organises separate counts), ducks and rails

This report covers the area occupied by the new local government councils of Stirling, Falkirk and Clackmannanshire (the 'region'). In total, 95 still water sites, 97.9 km of river and 22.6 km of canal were counted by 49 counters.

The following table consists of matched monthly data for total wildfowl on 25 major sites (20 still waters). Those sites holding fed Mallard have been excluded.

	1998/9	1999/0	2000/1	2001/2	2002/3
September	2592	2939	2110	2180	2633
October	2766	4426	3016	2934	3519
November	3625	4465	4565	4129	4526
December	4469	4824	4831	3758	4124
January	4377	4367	4419	3418	4234
February	3289	4155	3761	4274	3467
March	2302	2259	2478	2512	2432
Total	23420	27435	25180	23205	24935

This season's numbers are 2 % down on the average largely due to the lower figures for December to March.

Still Water Sites

Standing water in Central Region amounts to 7693 hectares or 2.9 % of the area.

The top ten individual sites along with monthly averages are listed below:– (previous season's figures in brackets)

	Site	Average	
1. (3)	Gartmorn Dam	450	(331)
2. (1)	Gart complex	395	(479)
3. (4)	Loch Earn	275	(316)
4. (5)	Airthrey Loch	260	(247)
5. (8)	L.Dochart-Iubhair	213	(168)
6. (2)	Lake of Menteith	209	(403)
7. (9)	Vale of Coustry	179	(159)
8. (6)	Kersiepow South Pond	173	(198)
9. (7)	Loch Venachar	164	(168)
10. (14)	Doune Ponds	128	(117)

The above table excludes sites where Mallard are reared and released for shooting. Gartmorn received its 250th WEBS count this year, although it has regained premier place the monthly average is only half the long term average. Marked falls occurred for Lake of Menteith and Blairdrummond Safari Park.

Linear Water Features: Rivers & Canals

This season coverage of the rivers length decreased somewhat, the most important gap being the stretch of the Forth about Kippen. Canal coverage was good but duck numbers affected by drainage and repair work. The most favoured river was the Forth above and below the Teith confluence with 28 birds km^{-1}, followed by the Teith with 26. In total numbers there are four stretches of the Forth that are equivalent to the waters in the lochs and ponds table. Canals scored at 3.7 km^{-1}.

SYSTEMATIC LIST

Codes – S, F and C indicate records from Stirling, Falkirk and Clackmannanshire "Districts".

RED-THROATED DIVER *Gavia stellata* (b,w)

F　　　Kinneil: from 2 on 6 Jan to 1 on 12 Apr, max 4 on 27 Jan; 1 on 27 Sep, then from 9 Nov to 22 Dec with a remarkable 17 on 24 Nov when parties of 9 & 5 flew high to W (DT). 1 Bo'ness 14 Oct. Skinflats Pools: from 26 Nov to 24 Dec with max in Dec of 5 on 12th & 13th. At Blackness from 6 Jan to 21 Apr, max 3 on 24 Feb & 24 Mar, 1 on 1/7 Dec & 1 Higgins Neuk on 31st (GO RJD MA AB DT). 1 Drumbowie Res 3 Dec (NB).

C　　　1 S.Alloa 26 Oct (RJD).

S　　　2 L.Katrine 22 Mar. 1 L.Ard 5 Dec (NB).

2001.S   2l flew W at Fallin 20 Nov (RJD) – this exceptional record foreshadows those from Kinneil in Nov 2002 (CJH).

*BLACK-THROATED DIVER *Gavia arctica* (b,w)

F　　　1 W.Grangemouth 13 Jan & 13 Dec (MVB).

S　　　Trossachs: pair noted at 1 site on 25/28 Apr; at a 2nd site on 28 Apr (DT DOE).

*GREAT NORTHERN DIVER *Gavia immer* (w)

F　　　1(lst winter) Skinflats Pools 12 to 26 Dec – lst record for this well watched site (GO AB RJD HC MVB AT).

2001.S   1 flew W with other divers at Fallin 20 Nov (RJD).

LITTLE GREBE *Tachybaptus ruficollis* (B,w)

　　　　WEBS max: 8 Forth estuary in Jan & 7 in Dec (DMB). 65 inland in Oct, still 62 in Dec (NB).

F　　　At Skinflats 3 Jan to 24 Feb, 28 Jul to 20 Dec, max 10 on 9 Jan & 13 on 13 Dec (GO AB MA et al). 1 AoT Larbert Pond, no evidence of breeding (AB). 3 Pr raised 6 Y at Drumbowie Res (NB).

S　　　Breeding season: 2 AoT L.Watston 15 Feb to 5 Jul, Pr Lanrick 30 Mar & Doune Lodge 4 May (CJH DOE); 2 AoT L.Walton 13 Apr –Juvs seen in Sep (DAC); 2 Pr fledged 2Y Airthrey (MVB). 7 L.Lubnaig 1 Jan (99 % ice), calling in Mar & Juv seen in Sep. In Dec 5 L.Voil/Doine & 9 L.Dochart/Iubhair (NB).

GREAT CRESTED GREBE *Podiceps cristatus* (b,W)

　　　　WEBS totals: 17 Forth estuary in Feb & 25 in Oct (DMB); 31 inland in Sep (only 7 in Dec) (NB).

F　　　Kinneil: 27 on 6 Jan; 1 on 5 Jul, 20 on 10 Aug, max 35 on 1 Dec; 112 Blackness 1 Jan, 33 on 7 Dec -*possibly same Dec flock as Kinneil, Ed* (DT MA et al).

C　　　Gartmorn: 6 on 14 Mar, juv in Sep; 3 on 24 Dec (AT).

S   In breeding season pairs noted at Lake of Menteith, L.Watston, Carron Valley Res (2Y), Blairdrummond, Pr Cambusmore 23 Mar nested despite disturbance but no Y (DT CJH DAC RKP PWS).

*RED-NECKED GREBE *Podiceps grisegena*
C   1 Gartmorn 1 Dec (AT). *Full description, 1st for Clackmannan.*

*SLAVONIAN GREBE *Podiceps auritus*
F   1 Bo'ness 20 Oct (DMB). 2 Skinflats Pools 12th & 27th Dec, single 13th to 17th (GO AT *et al*).
S   1 L.Katrine 19 Nov (NB).

FULMAR *Fulmarus glacialis* (p)
F   2 Blackness 6 Jan & 1 26 May. On 9 dates (27 birds) Kinneil from 28 Jun to 13 Sept, 10 on 6 Sep (MA DT GO).

*MANX SHEARWATER *Puffinus puffinus*
F   1 Kinneil 9 Sep (DT).

GANNET *Sula bassana* (p)
F   All Juvs: at Kinneil from 6th Sep to max of 5 on 28th (DT). 3 Blackness 22 Sep. 1 Skinflats 10 Oct (GO MA).

CORMORANT *Phalacrocorax carbo* (S,W)
    WEBS max: 170 Forth Estuary in Feb; 164 in Sep (DMB). 70 inland in Nov (NB).
F   45 Grangemouth (W) 8 Sep (MVB).
C   90 S.Alloa roost 20 Aug (MVB). Max Gartmorn 7 on 26 Mar & 24 Dec (AT)
S   13 Carron Valley Res 5 Oct & 14 L.Walton 3 Nov (DAC). 30 L.Lubnaig 29 Oct (DC). 13 N Third Res 19 Nov & 23 Lake of Menteith on 24th (BO NB).

*SHAG *Phalacrocorax aristotelis*
S   1 Juv on Teith at Lecropt 11 Dec (RJD), *2nd inland record (CJH).*

*LITTLE EGRET *Egretta garzetta*
F   1 Skinflats 21 to 24 Apr was lst for Upper Forth (AB GO) – followed by a bird (? same) 29 Nov to 15 Dec. Both birds photographed (GO AB MVB RJD HC AT NB).

Figure 1 Adult Little Egret in breeding plumage, Skinflats Pools April 21 to 24, 2002. First record for Upper Forth.
Photograph courtesy of G. Owens

Figure 2 Little Egret at Skinflats Pools, November 29 to December 15, 2002. (Autumn bird.)
Photograph courtesy of G. Owens

GREY HERON *Ardea cinerea* (B,W)
    WEBS max: 10 Forth Estuary in Jan & 29 in Oct (DMB). 85 inland in Oct (NB).
F   At least 12 nests Dunmore 14 Apr (AB). 14 Skinflats 8 Aug & 20 (max) on 20 Oct (GO MVB). 18 Kinneil 6 Sep (DT).
C   11 on Devon, Dollar-Alva, in Mar & 14 in Dec (GEL DE).
S   14 Lecropt 13 Jan (DT). 15 Blairdrummond 27 Feb (JNW).

MUTE SWAN   Cygnus olor (B,W)
WEBS max: 20 Forth Estuary in Feb (DMB). 195 inland in Dec (NB).
Groups totalling 55 in early autumn had 19 Juv. Two adults colour ringed as
cygnets: one at Callander on 26 Feb had been ringed near Kirkliston in Aug
1997, was at Hogganfield Loch through the winters of 98/99 & 99/00 and at Torry
Bay in Jan 2001; the other at Stirling on 3 Dec had been ringed at Glenrothes in
Aug 1999, in 2000 it was seen Cramond in Mar, then was at Hogganfield Loch
Apr to Aug. (NB).

F   29 at Skinflats floods 23 Feb, Pr nested on pools, eggs did not hatch; Ad + 5Y
on canal at Grangemouth 19 Jun – other Ad reported shot (AS GO AB).

C   2 Prs Cambus Pools, reared 5Y & 2Y, Pr + 3J Blackdevonmouth 29 Sep (CJH). 23
Gartmorn 14 Jan & 18 on 19 Oct, 3 nests (AT).

S   Max Lake of Menteith 21 on 19 Apr (RB). 19 Airthrey 23 Apr, Pr fledged 3Y
(MVB). Pr + 6Y L.Watston 5 Jul (CJH). 2 Prs Cambusmore 23 Mar (PWS). Juv at
Fallin 8 Nov was ringed Linlithgow in Jul (RJD).

WHOOPER SWAN   Cygnus cygnus (W)
% Juveniles: Jan/Feb 21 % (n=72); Oct-Dec 26 % (n = 95).

F   Scarce – 8 Camelon 28 Feb. 9 Carronshore 19 Oct (1st of autumn), 15 Skinflats 2
Nov (MA AB DAC).

C   20 Tullibody Inch 24 Mar only large group (DMB).

S   10 L Voil 21 Feb; 40 L.Dochart 6 Jan, 1 on 24 Apr - last of spring (PWS). On the
carse, only large spring herd was on Thornhill Carse from 5 Jan (69 – max) to 50
on 26 Mar. (DAC DT JNW). 1st of autumn were in October: 6 S.Alloa on 18th
& 2 Lecropt on 20th. Later in autumn large herds at Fallin from 6 Nov (when 1
ad killed by hitting wires), max 33 on 11th, & 30 on Thornhill Carse 23/24 Nov
(RJD DT RJ).

PINK-FOOTED GOOSE   Anser brachyrhynchus (W)
Feeding flocks reported from the Carse of Stirling and the Fallin to Skinflats
area in both winters but in the absence of coordinated counts it is difficult to
assess the total number of birds using the area. The October and November
national goose counts provide the best opportunity to do this but unfortunately
some roosts are not being counted at this time. In the first winter period 750
Flanders Moss on 8 Jan & 1250 Littleward on 16 Mar were the largest flocks on
the Carse (RJD HD DT), and 700 Throsk on 3 Jan and 2000 Alloa Inch on 24 Mar
the largest flocks east of Stirling (RJD HD DMB). 16 Skinflats on 22 Apr (GO)
and 7 Kinneil on 3 May (DT) the last flocks noted. In autumn 56 Skinflats and
98S Kinneil on 18 Sep (AB, DT) the first. The October goose count found 4515
Lake of Menteith on 13 Oct (SS) & 1900 Skinflats on 20 Oct (DMB) but Loch
Mahaick, the other main site at this time, was not counted. In November there
were 1470 Skinflats on 10th   (DMB), none at Loch Mahaick and Lake of
Menteith was not counted, but at least 1500 were found feeding on the Carse
that day (MVB).

BEAN GOOSE   Anser fabilis (W)
F   On Slamannan plateau: 192 on 12 Jan; 1st of autumn on 6 Oct, record flock of
232 on 26 Oct (B.G Study Group).

WHITEFRONTED GOOSE   Anser albifrons
2001. C 1 (Greenland race) Cambus 13 Jan (RJD).

GREYLAG GOOSE   Anser anser (b,W)
The largest flocks in 2002 were early in the year with 500 on the upper Forth in
Feb & Mar, and in the lower Devon valley, where 452 at Coalsnaughton on 7 Jan
and 350 on 8 Feb (DR AT GEL) was a high count, still 183 Clackmannan on 10
Apr. 128 Glen Dochart 29 Jan and 100 on 7 Mar (NB PWS) were other notable

records in the first winter period whilst inland in Falkirk were 121 Slamannan 6 Feb and 100 L.Ellrig on the 13th (NB JN).
40 South Alloa on 3 Sep (RJD) must have been feral birds, 13 ->S Skinflats on 3 Oct (AB) & 93 L.Coulter on 4th were probably Icelandic migrants. The November goose count found 252 feeding on the Carse of Stirling and 250 roosting at South Alloa. The latter flock fed at Menstrie and Blackgrange at this time with 235 Blackgrange on 24 Nov (RJD). North of the carse there were 115 at Gart 15 Jan & 163 on 5 Dec, 144 Dochart Haughs on 9 Dec and 200 Ardeonaig, Loch Tay, on 27 Nov (NB PWS).

CANADA GOOSE *Branta canadensis* (b,W)
  WEBS inland recorded 445 in Oct (NB).
F 10 Throsk on 3 Jan (RJD) and 15 Skinflats on 25 Aug (AB). 41 St Helens Loch 23 Nov (MA).
S Becoming increasingly numerous on the Carse of Stirling with 280 Blairdrummond G.Pit on 7 Sep and 200 Cambusmore on 9 Nov (MVB PWS) the largest flocks. 40 Loch Katrine on 15 Jan (CS) were unusually far west. Spring/summer: single pairs Loch Watston and Loch Arklet, broods of 2 & 5 goslings Lake of Menteith on 11 May (DT CJH RB).

BARNACLE GOOSE *Branta leucopsis* (w)
F 3 Alloa Inch on 24 Mar & 1 Blackgrange on 30 Mar (DMB RJD HD). 53 ->S Kinneil on 28 Sep (DT) the first of the autumn and the largest flock of the year. 1Skinflats 12 Jan & 2 on 20 Oct, 4 Throsk on 26 Oct, 1 Skinflats on 5 Nov (MA MVB RJD MA GO).
S 1 Frew Toll on 10/24 Feb (DT DR).
2001.C/S 4 Cambus 27 Jan, last 1 on 21 Apr. 2 Fallin 22 Nov (RJD).

BRENT GOOSE *Branta bernicla* (w)
F 1 pale bellied at Skinflats 16 to 20 Oct (GO MV RJD).

SHELDUCK *Tadorna tadorna* (b,W)
  WEBS max: 244 Forth Estuary in Jan & 2849 in Sep (DMB).
F Moult flock at Kinneil totalled 2577 on 24 Aug; 649 on 8 Jun. (DMB); 1000 Skinflats 8 Sep, only 219 on 15 Dec (MVB). Inland, 1 juv Lathallan pond 16 Sep & 7 Oct (JW)
C 1 on Devon at Alva 27 Jan (GEL). F+4Y Blackdevon Wetlands. 50 Tullibody Inch 13 Jul included a creche of 11(CJH).
S Max 9 on Forth above Fallin 17 Feb (DJ).

WIGEON *Anas penelope* (b,W)
  WEBS max: 451 Forth Estuary in Feb & 537 in Dec (DMB); 896 inland in Nov (NB).
F 220 Blackness 7 Dec. Kinneil: max 500 on 6 Jan, 75 on 12 Apr & 1 on 10th May; 1st of autumn were 72 on 9 Sep, 250 on 15 Dec (DT GO).
C 178 Alva floods 10 Feb & 60 Kersiepow 11 Dec (NB). F Cambus 1 Jun (CJH). 100 Alloa Inches 10 Oct (RJD). Counts at two sites in Feb showed a sex ratio of 60 % M (n=188) (AT).
S Gart Lochs (Cambusmore): 321 on 12 Feb; 259 on 15 Nov. 79 L.Dochart 24 Feb & 90 on 9 Dec. 116 L.Venachar 24 Oct (NB). 150 Lecropt 5 Jan & 170 on 21 Dec (DT). Max on the upper Forth between the Teith and Gargunnock 476 (incl. 62 at Frew) in Feb & 255 in Nov (RC DR). F L.Watston 17 Jul (DOE).

*GADWALL *Anas strepera*
F M Kinneil 12 Apr (DT).
C Pr Gartmorn 14 Jan, M 2 Feb to 17 Apr. M Cambus Pools 14 Mar, Pr on 8 & 30 Apr & M on 24th (AT DAC CJH). Pr Alloa Inch 24 Mar (DMB).
S 3 Doune Lodge 29 Mar (DOE).

TEAL *Anas crecca* (b,W)
WEBS max: 815 Forth Estuary in Feb & 1086 in Oct (DMB). 1515 inland in Nov (NB).
F   Kinneil: still 180 on 12 Apr; 65 on 15 Aug rising to 450 on 2 Nov. Skinflats: 178 on 13 Jan, 9M on 28 Jun; 50 on 26 Aug & 228 on 15 Dec. Inland max 145 Carronshore in Jan & 55 on 6 Oct (DT MVB GO AB IH).
C   On Devon: 91 Dollar –Alva in Feb, 119 Dollar-Tillicoultry 21 Dec. 127 Kersiepow 20 Jan & 162 on 22 Nov (DE GEL NB). F Cambus Pools 1 Jun (CJH).
S   263 Gart 12 Feb & 239 on 15 Nov. 103 L.Mahaick 24 Sep. 118 L.Dochart 7 Oct (NB). 200 Flanders Moss 30 Jan & 140 on 8 Nov (DP). 525 on Forth below Gargunnock 14 Feb & 247 on 17 Nov (RC). 317 on Forth, Fallin to Cambus-kenneth in Nov (DJ AT). Pr Carron Valley Res 23 Apr (DAC).

MALLARD *Anas platyrhynchos* (B,W)
WEBS max: 229 Forth Estuary in Feb & 371 in Dec (DMB), 2058 inland in Nov (NB).
F   60 Pow Burn 1 Sep (RJD). 53 Carronshore 13 Jan & 49 on 6 Oct (AB).
C   243 Kersiepow 20 Sep (NB). 221 Gartmorn 24 Dec (AT).
S   272 Airthrey 10 Feb & 271 on 6 Oct (MK). 120 Dochart Haughs 29 Mar (NB). 297 on Forth below Gargunnock 15 Sep (RC). 346 on Teith 11 Dec, many released birds (RJD).

*GARGANEY *Anas querquedula*
F   Pr Skinflats 14 & 19 May (MA GO AB).

PINTAIL *Anas acuta* (W)
F   Skinflats/Carronmouth max 46 on 10 Feb & 47 on 15 Dec, last of spring Pr on 13 Apr; 1 on 30 Sep & 15 on 20 Oct. More than usual at Kinneil: 27 on 17 Feb; 1st autumn on 8 Sep (20), max 79 on 23 Oct & 92 on 2 Nov (MVB GO AB DMB DT).
S   2 Kinbuck 9 Mar; 1 Fallin 7 Sep & 1 Gart 15 Nov (DOE RJD NB).

				Area Summary				
Jan	Feb	Mar	Apr	-	Aug	Sep	Oct	Nov	Dec
36	73	23	7		0	22	94	118	47

The high estimate in Nov & the low in Dec probably reflect movement between Skinflats & Kinneil: no Kinneil counts available for Dec.

SHOVELER *Anas clypeata* (p)
F   Kinneil: 2 on 1 Jan & 17 Feb; 1 on 4 Aug & 6 on 17th, max of 7 on 21 Sep & 21 on 26 Oct, last 7 on 15 Dec. 1 Skinflats: 9 Aug (MA DT DMB GO).
C   Pr Blackdevon Wetlands 16 Apr. 3 Alloa Inch 24 Mar & 24 on 22 Aug (CJH DMB).
S   1 L.Watston 17 Oct & 3 on 9 Nov (CJH DOE).

POCHARD *Aythya ferina* (W)
WEBS max: 145 inland in Nov (NB).
F   Autumn return 8 Kinneil 4 Aug & 4 S.Alloa on 1 Oct (DT RJD). 64 St Helens Loch 4 Nov (NB).
C   Gartmorn: autumn return, F on 15 Sep, 13 on 24 Dec; M on 26 May (RJD AT).
S   39 L.Ard 24 Jan & 28 on 5 Dec. 34 Lake of Menteith 8 Jan & 49 on 15 Feb. 19 Gart 12 Mar & 16 on 6 Dec (NB). 12 Carron Valley Res 21 Dec; 12 L.Walton 3 Nov (DAC).

TUFTED DUCK *Aythya fuligula* (B,W)
WEBS max: 350 inland in Nov (NB).
F   57 Black Loch 3 Sep. St Helens Loch 4 Nov (NB). 6 Skinflats 22 Apr. 4 Kinneil 3 May & 5 on 28 Jun. (GO DT). 14 Larbert Pond 6 Apr, 2 Prs 28 May & 2 M on 23 Jun (AB).
C   78 Gartmorn 14 Mar, still 69 (27F) on 17 Apr; 104 on 9 Sep & 117 Oct/ Nov (AT).

Pr Blackdevon Wetlands 16 Apr & Pr Cambus 1 Jun (CJH).

S 50 Blairdrummond (Coustry) 12 Mar, 122 on 7 Sep & 44 on 22 Dec (97 % ice). 37 Lake of Menteith 17 Mar (NB MVB). 27 L.Watston 13 Mar, broods of 7 & 4 on 5 Jul (CJH). Max Airthrey only 23 on 10 Feb (MK).

SCAUP *Aythya marila* (w)

F Kinneil: F on 12-14 Apr, 5 (2M) 3 May & Pr on 31st; from 6 Sep to 24 Nov (max 2). Skinflats: 1M Skinflats Pools 16 Jul, 31 Oct, 27 & 31 Dec (DT GO DMB MVB AT).

EIDER *Somateria mollissima* (w)

F At Blackness 3 Feb to 21 Apr, max 21(14M) on 31 Mar (MA). At Kinneil 17 Feb to 3 May (max 2 Pr on 16 Apr); from 9 Nov to 1 Dec (when max 3 Pr) (DT). 2 Skinflats 8 Jun (DMB).

*LONG-TAILED DUCK *Clangula hyemalis*

F 1 (F/Imm) Kinneil 16 to 31 Oct (RJD DMB DT GO). 1 Faughlin Res (Carron Bridge) 3 Dec (NB) *odd since Res is only 4Ha (CJH).*

*COMMON (BLACK) SCOTER *Melanitta nigra*

F M Kinneil 4 Aug (DT).

GOLDENEYE *Bucephula clangula* (W)

WEBS max: 38 Forth Estuary in Feb & 65 in Dec (DMB). 365 inland in Dec (NB). Sex ratio counts from distinct sites in Jan-Mar showed 24 % M (n=351).

Few summering birds – eclipse M at Gartmorn 8 Jun (DAC), & late autumn return – 1st on 28 Sep at Kinneil (DT).

F Max at Skinflats 28 on 2 Mar, 25 on 19 Oct to 9 Nov (MA AB DT). 21 Bo'ness 20 Oct (DMB). 31 Black Loch 4 Mar (NB).

C 35 Tullibody Inch 24 Mar, 52 Fallin-Dunmore 21 Dec (DMB GO AB). 71 Gartmorn 17 Feb & 57 on 23 Nov (AT). 95 on lower Devon (Tillicoultry to Cambus) in Jan, 116 in Dec (GEL KW PD).

S 38 on Forth, Forthbank-Stirling 19 Jan, 57 on 23 Nov (AT). 103 Lake of Menteith 15 Feb (still 39 on 19 Apr), 48 on 24 Nov. 40 L.Venachar 17 Dec. 54 L.Dochart/Iubhair 24 Feb, 44 on 9 Dec (NB RB). 37 Carron Valley Res 2 Mar, 34 on 21 Dec (DAC).

*SMEW *Mergus albellus* (w)

S M at L.Dochart/Iubhair from 2 Jan to 9 Feb (DOE PWS NB DT). *This regular winterer did not reappear this autumn (CJH).*

RED-BREASTED MERGANSER *Mergus serrator* (B,W)

23 Forth Estuary in Feb & 37 in Oct (DMB).

F Skinflats: 5 on 23 Apr; 16 on 14 Oct. Few at Kinneil except 23 on 14 Apr (GO).

C 4 Delph (Tullibody) Pond 10 Feb increasing to 13 (7M) in mid-Mar; birds tame, dived frequently & occasional display (NB AD). *An unusual event, especially since the pond is small & heavily used by walkers & dogs (CJH).*

S Pr Airthrey 23 Mar (DMB). Pr L.Katrine 12 May (DAC).

GOOSANDER *Mergus merganser* (B,W)

WEBS max: 103 inland in Oct. 4 on estuary in Feb & 20 in Oct (NB DMB). 1st Ms in autumn were 4 (flock 10) at Cambuskenneth 20 Oct, 12 Airthrey on 13 Nov, 1 Grangemouth on 15th & 5 L.Katrine on 19th (AT MVB AS NB). Sex ratio counts from distinct sites in Jan-Mar showed 54 % M (n=72).

F 15 Kinneil 3 May were late (DT). 1st of autumn 6 Skinflats 28 Jul, max 26 on 14 Oct (AB GO MA).

C 12 on lower Devon (Dollar to Cambus) in Dec (DE KW).

S 25 on Forth, Forthbank to Teith in Feb, 23 above Stirling Bridge on 14 Apr, 15 Fallin 30 Mar (AB AT RJD), no other river counts above 12. 37 Airthrey 5 Feb &

48 C.J. Henty & A.E. Thiel

20 on 13 Nov (MVB), 22 Coustry 31 Oct. 2Pr L.Ard 22 Mar, 2Pr L.Voil & 2Pr L
Lubnaig 1 Apr; 6 L.Katrine 21 Jul (NB DOE DAC).
RUDDY DUCK *Oxyura jamaicensis* (w)
   No records.
*HONEY BUZZARD *Pernis apivorus*
S   A bird fledged from a Speyside nest and fitted with a radio transmitter was
      recorded near N.Third Res on the p.m of 17 September (having been earlier
      tracked in G.Lednock) and again close by on the a.m of the 19th; on the 20th it
      was near Lanark, some 45 km south (R H Dennis). *This is a unique record : the first
      time any species has been reliably reported without anyone seeing or hearing it, and
      without leaving any physical traces (CJH). On 22 Sep this bird had reached S.Wales but
      then, with strong easterly winds, headed out over the Atlantic and, in one continuous
      flight, got to south of Madeira where it stopped, probably drowned on the 27th. At this
      time its father (also radiotagged) had crossed the Sahara to Mali and went on to winter
      in Gabon.*
RED KITE *Milvus milvus*
      The RSPB/Scottish Natural Heritage re-establishment scheme continues with a
      max winter roost of 49 on 1 Jan and 45 on 12 Dec; however, 86 marked
      individuals were detected, 12 from Black Isle and 1 from Dumfries. Seventeen
      AoTs, fourteen pairs attempted clutches but four failed in egg stage during bad
      weather; ten pairs raised 22 or 23Y. (DOE). Please try to note wing tag colours
      on any bird you may see, Ed.
      Many reports Braes of Doune between Callander (25 Apr) & Lecropt (4 on 13
      Feb); max away from roost was 7 on 27 Mar. To the west, 2 at Spout of
      Ballochleam 30 Mar & 1 Flanders Moss 16 Jun (DT DAC DP RJD HC J.Rae).
*MARSH HARRIER *Circus aeruginosus*
F   An immature bird(s) at Kinneil on 6 & 9 Sep and at Skinflats on the 13th & 15th
      (DT RJD HC C Bowden). 1F Skinflats 14 May (MA).
HEN HARRIER *Circus cyaneus* (b, w)
      11 males and 5 Ringtails noted.
F   M Skinflats 23 Oct (GO). 1 L.Ellrig 12 Dec (JN).
C   1 Glenquey 24 Nov (MVB). M Tillicoultry (Kirk Crags) 22 Dec (MA).
S   Six singles on Carse of Stirling 19 Jan to 24 Feb and 5 from 8 Sep to 24 Nov. Also
      8 records Feb/Mar & Sep/Dec on surrounding hill ground & Strathallan. M
      Gargunnock Hills 17 Apr (RJD HC DJC DP DT GJB AW MVB DOE).
*GOSHAWK *Accipiter gentilis*
S   1 Thornhill 28 Oct (DC).
SPARROWHAWK *Accipiter nisus* (B,W)
      Many records throughout area, mainly Jan-Mar & Aug-Dec. WEBS counts
      recorded 22 Sparrowhawks as opposed to 80 Kestrels (NB). Caught Starling at
      Fallin & Blackbird at Bo'ness, struck Feral Pigeon at Bo'ness; mobbed by
      corvids, Pied Wagtails & hirundines (RJD HC AS et al). 4 prs Doune, 2+2+4 prs
      at 3 sites on Braes of Doune (DOE). All year at Skinflats, did not nest (GO AB).
BUZZARD *Buteo buteo* (B,W)
      As breeding bird: widespread S & C, breeding regularly & generally more
      frequent F.
F   Noted in breeding season at Torwood, Camelon (6 on 7 Apr), Wallacebank
      Wood. At Skinflats through year, no nest (AB MA AS GO). Regular over Kinneil-
      Bo'ness, mainly Jan/Feb & Oct-Dec, but max 10 Kinneil 1 Apr & 5 on 5 May &
      25 Aug (AS DT GO).
C   Noted in breeding season at Dollar Glen, Muckhart, Tillicoultry, Alva, Fishcross,
      Cambus, Gartmorn Dam, Forest Mill, Blackdevonmouth, Kennetpans (AT).

S   19 AoT found Callander to Doune (about 1 pr per sq km); 15 pr checked, 13 successful & raised 31 Y (DOE DA). Large groups in breeding range, Jan-Apr, were 17 Doune, 16 Lecropt & Braes of Doune; also 5 over Stirling 29 Mar & 6 L.Walton 13 Apr (DOE DT DP DAC).

GOLDEN EAGLE *Aquila chrysaetos* (b,w)
S   8 ranges checked, 6 occupied by pairs, 1 by a singleton, & also signs of prescence on the last. Only 2 successful pairs, reared 2Y (PSA). 1 G.Lochay 20 Jun, 1 Strathyre 17 Jul mobbed by 2 Ravens (PWS DC).

OSPREY *Pandion haliaetus*
      1st of year at Doune on 29 Mar, then Lake of Menteith on 3 Apr, a pair at a Trossachs site on 8 Apr & one at Carron Valley Res on the 9th (DOE DT).
F   1 over Skinflats 21 Aug, chased away by gulls and crows (GO).
S   Ten pairs bred but 4 failed due to heavy rain in late spring, 6 pairs raised 10Y (DOE).
      1 Lecropt 21 Apr & 8 May; 1 L.Mahaick 7 May. 4 Carron Valley Res 16 Jun, 3 on 28 Jun & 1 on 21 Aug (DT NB DMB RKP GO).

KESTREL *Falco tinnunculus* (B,W)
      Difficult to make significant observations, hence generally under-recorded.
F   Reported through year at many sites Airth to Blackness (AS).
S   4 Prs around Doune & 2 Prs on Braes of Doune at Drumloist (DOE).

MERLIN *Falco columbarius* (b?,w)
      9 F/J noted to 2 M.
F   Skinflats: 1 on 8 & 13 Jan, 13-20 Feb & 14 Apr; 1 on 20 Oct & 15 Dec (GO MVB AB). 1 Kinneil 27 Oct & 24 Nov (DT).
S   Pr (AoT) Lochearnhead 4 Apr (DC). 1 Lecropt 13 Jan, 25 Sep & 20 Oct. 1 Lake of Menteith 26 Mar. 1 Thornhill 28 Oct & 1 Carron Valley 22 Dec (DT MVB DAC).

PEREGRINE *Falco peregrinus* (B,W)
F   1 S.Alloa 19/29 Oct; 1 Airth 1 Sep & 11 Oct; 1 Skinflats 3 Oct & 1 Kinneil on 20th (RJD AB). 1 Falkirk 3 Mar & 14 Sep. 1 Blackness 22 Sep (MA).
S&C   31 territories checked, 24 occupied (23 pairs, 1 single) - high numbers due to intensive national survey. 9 successful pairs reared 17 Y, poor success in poor weather (PSA).
      On lower ground, Plean to Thornhill, 14 records mainly Jan-Mar (6) and Oct/Nov (6), but 1 Fallin 2 Jun & 2 on 16 Jul. Predation included Feral Pigeon, also eating prey on wing & then chasing Fieldfares (RJD HC DT DC DOE).

RED GROUSE *Lagopus lagopus* (B,W)
      Generally under-recorded.
S   present on site of proposed Braes of Doune windfarm (c 520 Ha) but estimates of AoTs vary – 3 in 2001 but 21 in 2002 (RSPB).

BLACK GROUSE *Tetrao tetrix* (B,W)
S   Reported from Cairnoch Hill (Carron Valley) in Jan & Feb (lek calls), also Doune Lodge in Apr (RJD HC DOE).

GREY PARTRIDGE *Perdix perdix* (B,W).
F   5 Kinneil 19 Jan (DT). Max Skinflats 3 Ad + 8Y on 29 Jun (GO). 8 Camelon 2 Jan & 14 on 10 Feb (MA).
S   2 Blairlogie 6 Feb (CJH). 2 Fallin 2 Mar & 1 S.Alloa 30 Jul (RJD).
2001.S Bred Fallin, max 15 on 29 Aug (RJD).

PHEASANT *Phasianus colchicus* (B,W)
      Abundant (usually by releases) on fields next to keepered estates.
F   Through year Skinflats, max M+2F 27 Mar (GO).
S   35 Blairdrummond Carse 27 Oct (MVB).

WATER RAIL *Rallus aquaticus* (w)
F   1 Skinflats 19 May. 1 Kinneil 24 Dec (GO). 1 Grangemouth 20 Oct (DMB).
C   1 Cambus Pools 1 Jun & 4 Nov (CJH RJD). At Tullibody Inch 20 Aug to Oct, max 4 on 15 Sep (DMB).
S   Heard at Balquhidder (L.Occasional) in spring, at least 2 on 27 May. 1 Blackwater Marshes 16 Jul (CE CJH).

MOORHEN *Gallinula chloropus* (B,W)
       WEBS max: 184 in Oct (NB).
F   6 Skinflats 16 Jul (GO). Bred Larbert Pond (2 Prs) & Dunmore (2 Prs) (AB RJD). 14 on Carron at Carronshore in Jan & Nov (AB MA). Max on Union Canal Polmont-Avon 13 in Nov (JW PD). 13 on Forth-Clyde canal Grangemouth-Bonnybridge in Oct. 25 Callendar Park 15 Jan & 29 on 17 Oct (AA DMM).
C   Cambus: 3 AoT W. Pool & 1 AoT E.Pool (CJH). Possibly 25 on lower Devon, Dollar-Menstrie *estimated from different WEBS counts of DE GEL & PD (CJH).*
S   1 Killin marshes 22 Apr (PWS). 2 AoT L.Watston 28 May (CJH). 6 Airthrey 3 Mar, nests attempted but none left by 16 Jul (MK MVB)

COOT *Fulica atra* (B,W)
       WEBS max: 521 in Dec (NB).
F   2 Skinflats 13 Mar - spring arrival, 2 AoT 25 Apr (GO). 3 AoT Larbert Pond Apr-Jun (AB).
C   Cambus: 2 AoT W. Pool & 1 AoT E.Pool. 3 AoT Blackdevonmouth 16 Apr (CJH). 124 Gartmorn Dam 14 Jan, 240 on 24 Dec (AT).
S   18 Airthrey 4 Feb, nests attempted but none left by 16 Jul (MVB). 5 AoT L.Watston 28 May (CJH). 167 Lake of Menteith 27 Jan, 74 on 15 Dec. 94 L.Coulter 3 Dec (NB). Nest in gullery Ashfield 18 Jun (DP).

OYSTERCATCHER *Haematopus ostralegus* (B,W)
       107 on Forth Estuary in Jan & 202 in Dec (DMB).
       Apart from 1 Lecropt on 19 Jan, spring return inland in February: Ashfield on 6th, L.Dochart 9th, Lecropt 10th (101), Doune 11th, Gartmorn 17th, L.Tay 26th (DT DP DOE AT PWS). Still on breeding ground Airthrey 25 Jul (CJH).
F   60 Kinneil 17 Feb & 114 on 9 Nov; 172 Blackness 24 Feb & 205 on 1 Dec (DT MA).
S   320 Lecropt on 24 Feb & only 120 on 3 Mar. 344 Blairdrummond on 12 Mar & 200 Cambusmore on 23rd (PWS DT NB). 12 ->SSW Dunblane on 3 Jul, return passage (MVB).

RINGED PLOVER *Charadrius hiaticula* (b,W)
       14 Forth Estuary in Jan & 23 in Sep (DMB).
F   Skinflats: 85 on 18 May & 82 on 19th; 3 on 9 Jul & 11 on 9 Aug (DMB GO RJD). 13 Kinneil 14 Jul & 22 on 9 Nov (DT). 18 W.Grangemouth 8 Sep (MVB). 30 Blackness 22 Sep & 55 on 1 Sep (MA).
C   2 in setaside by R.Devon (Marchglen) on 5 May, with 4Y on 25th (AT). *1st proved breeding in lowland Clacks (CJH).*
S   1 Carron Valley Res 2 Mar, 1 Callander on 12th & 2 Touch 4 Res on 24th (DAC NB AM). Pr Cambusmore 7 Apr, Pr G.Finglas 18 May (DOE).

GOLDEN PLOVER *Pluvialis apricaria* (B,W)
       199 on Forth estuary in Feb & 1200 in Dec (DMB).
F   Skinflats: 1st return 3 on 5 Jul & 9 on 18th, increasing to 32 on 21 Aug, 212 on 22 Sep & 500 on 19 Nov. 300 Kinneil 27 Jan, 600 on 26 Oct & 1700 on 24 Nov. 200 Higgins Neuk 14 Oct (GO AB MA DMB DT CJH RJD).
S   1 G.Kendrum 3 Apr, 42 Braes of Doune (Severie) 27 Apr, only 6 on 13 May (DC DOE). 150 Lecropt 21 Apr (DT).

GREY PLOVER *Pluvialis squatarola* (W)
F   Scarce on estuary. 7 Blackness 1 Jan & 6 on 27 Oct. Skinflats: 5 on 12 Jan; Spring passage max 5 on 19 May; 1st return 5 on 8 Aug, 14 on 20 Oct (MA GO MVB).

LAPWING *Vanellus vanellus* (B,W)
1048 on Forth Estuary in Jan & 2815 in Sep (DMB).
F   Kinneil: 400 on 27 Jan & 300 on 17 Feb; 60 on 28 Jun increasing to 400 on 4 Aug, 900 on 28 Sep & 1150 on 15 Dec. Skinflats: 350 on 27 Jan & 130 on 23 Feb; 1 AoT; 25 on 3 Jul to 450 on 26th, 1280 on 8 Sep & 1047 on 15 Oct (DT DMB AS AB DC et al). Inland return: 60 Bonnybridge 10 Feb (MA).
C   6 broods (17Y) in setaside by R.Devon (Marchglen) 25 May. 6 AoT Blackdevon Wetlands 16 Apr. 4 AoT Cambus 19 Jun. 650 Tullibody Inch 13 Jul 7 & 1050 on 20 Aug. 450 Cambus on 7 Sep. (AT CJH MVB RJD).
S   Spring return: 630 Lecropt & 200 Doune 24 Feb, 400 Ashfield on 25th & 150 Kinbuck on 26th. AoTs in Mar/Apr, Braes of Doune: 6 Dalbrack, 30 Severie, 12 Waterside (MVB DP DOE).

KNOT *Calidris canutus* (W)
3500 Forth Estuary in Jan & 3080 in Dec (DMB).
F   2000 Kinneil 6 Jan; 1st adult 21 Jul; 40 on 4 Aug & 175 on 31st; 4500 on 31 Dec. Very few Skinflats, incl. 11 on 8 May & 1st of autumn on 29 Jun (DT MVB GO). 3500 Blackness 8 Dec (MA).

*SANDERLING *Calidris alba* (p)
F   1 Skinflats 19 Jul. 8 Bo'ness 18 Oct (GO).

*LITTLE STINT *Calidris minutus*
F   1 Skinflats 11 Sep & 1 Kinneil on 28 Sep (AB DT).

*CURLEW SANDPIPER *Calidris ferruginea* (p)
F   Skinflats: In Sep, 8 on 8th & 1 on 11th; 2 imm on 5 Oct. 2 Kinneil 18 & 21 Sep, 3 on 28th (MVB AB GO DT).

DUNLIN *Calidris alpina* (b?,W)
9970 Forth Estuary in Jan & 8616 in Dec (DMB).
F   2500 Kinneil 6 Jan & 1000 on 28 Sep. Skinflats: 6970 on 13 Jan, last of spring 9 on 17 May; return from 4 Ad on 3 Jul, 150 on 11 Sept & 300 on 6 Oct, 3550 on 15 Dec (DT MVB GO AB CJH).

RUFF *Philomachus pugnax* (p)
F   Skinflats: 1st of autumn 28 Jun, 3 on 9 Jul then regular to 20 Oct, max of 4 on 11 Sep & 20 Oct; 1 on 20 Dec. 1 Kinneil 4 Aug then to 20 Oct with 2 on 5 & 9 Sep. (RJD DOE GO MA AB DT et al).
C   4 Alloa Inch on 19 Aug & 7 on 22nd (DMB).

Area Summary (half monthly)

Jul	Aug	Sep	Oct
3 1	2 11	6 4	3 5

JACK SNIPE *Lymnocryptes minimus* (w)
F   3 Grangemouth 20 Oct & 1 S.Alloa on 26th. 1 Kinneil 24 Nov & 5 on 24 Dec. 1 Skinflats 7 Dec. (DMB RJD DT GO).
S   1 Lecropt 5 Jan & 2 on 10/23 Feb; 2 on 20 Oct & 6 on 14 Dec (DT). 1 L.Ruskie 9 Oct & 1 Flanders Moss 27 Nov (NB DP).

SNIPE *Gallinago gallinago* (B,W)
Probably under-recorded in breeding season but may have decreased (CJH).
F   Max Kinneil 23 (on old tip) 24 Nov (DT). At Skinflats from 23 Jul, max 10 on 11 Sep & 11 on 1 Dec. 12 on Dunmore saltmarsh 21 Dec (GO AB). 10 S.Alloa 26 Oct, 9 Dunmore 27 Nov (RJD). 58 St Helen's Loch 3 Sep (NB).
C   9 Marchglen 3 Mar & 8 (poss. many more) on 7 Apr; only 1 site in May/Jun (AT). 17 Tullibody Inch 15 Sep (DMB).

S Lecropt: max 56 on 10 & 23 Feb, still 41 on 10 Mar; 32 on 10 Nov & 14 Dec (DT). Cambuskenneth: 20 on 20 Feb & 30 on 10 Mar; 31 on 23 Nov (AT). 21 Thornhill 15 Feb & 35 Blairdrummond (Coustry) 12 Mar (NB). 9 Carron Valley Res 5 Oct (DAC). 6 drumming Balquhidder (L.Occasional) 27 May (CJH). 1 G.Kendrum 11 Apr (JHA).

WOODCOCK *Scolopax rusticola* (B,W)
Under-recorded (Ed).
Roding noted Dunblane 18 Jun (MVB). Recorded from Achray Forest & Gargunnock to Alloa, Airth & Larbert at 11 sites Jan/Mar and 7 in Nov/Dec. 1 seen on road Cromlix & 1 roadkill Airth. 1 over Stirling 9 Nov, seen in streetlights. (DT RJD MA et al).

BLACK-TAILED GODWIT *Limosa limosa* (W)
F A spectacular spring migration between 21st and 26th April gave the largest flock ever recorded, 495 at Skinflats on the 24th; in the same movement there were also 25 at the Balvag marshes (L.Occasional, Balquhidder) on the 22nd and 50 at Killin (L.Tay) on the 26th – vanished by the next day (MA GO AB DC KE PWS). Before this there were only modest numbers with no records at all between mid-Jan and mid-Mar, there were also none between 13th May and 27th June. In the autumn numbers built up to a plateau level by early September and remained fairly high at both Kinneil & Skinflats until the end of the year, with 73 % at Kinneil. Low numbers in early October and early December are probably due to reduced observation. The only records from sites away from Grangemouth were 16 on 15th September at Tullibody Inch, 70 Blackness 27 Oct and a few around the Pow Burn. (DT DMB MA RJD *et al*).

Site Summary (half monthly)

	Jan	Feb	Mar	Apr	May	Jun	Jul	Aug	Sep	Oct		Nov		Dec	
Sknf			25	28 495	17	15	19 28	57 26	104		4	145 67	1	17	
Kinn	26			54	18	7	3 53	91 164	150 270	15 290	140			103	
Area Total	32		25	28 624	35	22	22 81	148 193	270 270	19 364	286 67	1	120		

BAR-TAILED GODWIT *Limosa lapponica* (W)
111 Forth Estuary in Jan & 330 in Dec (DMB).
F Kinneil: 160 on 6 Jan; lst of autumn 24 Jul, 330 on 15 Dec. Skinflats: lst of autumn 8 Jul, 51 on 8 Sep (DT GO DMB MVB). 159 Blackness 1 Dec (MA). 1 flew E at S.Alloa 3 Sep (RJD).

WHIMBREL *Numenius phaeopus* (p)
F One spring record, Kinneil on 10 May. 1st of autumn, 1 Kinneil 28 Jun; last, 2 Skinflats 6 Oct (GO DT AB MVB).
C 1 Inches 20 & 22 Aug (DMB MVB).

CURLEW *Numenius arquata* (B,W)
868 on Forth estuary in Feb & 648 in Dec (DMB).
F Skinflats: 175 on 21 Jan, 400 on 10 Feb; 227 on 8 Sep. Kinneil:130 on 28 Mar; 150 on 28 Jun, 350 on 21 Jul & 450 on 11 Sep. 300 Airth 20 Jan (AS MVB DT). 125 Blackness 27 Jan & 400 on 24 Feb (MA). 163 Lathallan 3 Mar (JW).
C 140 Cambus 28 Feb & 223 on 15 Dec. 102 Kennetpans 25 Mar (DP CJH AT).
S Spring return 70 Lecropt on 3 Mar & 116 on 12th, 143 Gart on 12 Mar (DT DC NB). On Braes of Doune 6 AoT Severie & 10 Waterside in Apr (DOE).

SPOTTED REDSHANK *Tringa erythropus* (p)
F 1 Skinflats 28 Jul to 13 Sep. 1 Kinneil 10 May & 1 on 18/21 Sep (GO RJD AB DT).

REDSHANK *Tringa totanus* (B,W)
1381 Forth Estuary in Feb & 2442 in Oct (DMB).
lst spring return R.Devon 9 Mar, Cambusmore on 7 Apr & Killin on 8th (20 on 10th), L.Walton on 13th (GEL DOE PWS DAC).

F   Skinflats: 546 on 13 Jan, still 300 on 13 Apr; 75 on 3 Jul, 860 on 8 Sep & 695 on 15 Dec. Kinneil: 320 on 28 Mar & 600 on 12 Apr; 100 on 5 Jul & 600 on 21st, 1250 on 20 Oct. 34 Pow Burn 14 Oct (MVB AB RJD HC DT DMB).

C   4 AoT 5 Jun Blackdevon Wetlands (CJH).

On Braes of Doune 1 AoT Dalbrack on 6 Apr & 2 AoT Severie on 7th (DOE).

GREENSHANK *Tringa nebularia* (p)

F   Skinflats: 1 from 10 Jan to 12 Mar; autumn from 27 Jun to 17 Dec (max 7 on 22 Sep & 6 on 5 Oct). At Kinneil 21 Jul to 26 Oct, max 8 on 18 Sep. (AB GO AT MVB DT MA).

C   3 Alloa Inches 20 Aug & 1 on 22nd (MVB DMB).

S   1 Killin 10 Apr (PWS), 2 on Forth at Gargunnock 16 Apr (SE).

Area Summary (half monthly, autumn passage)

Jul	Aug	Sep	Oct	Nov
3	5 11	9 15	9 2	2 1

GREEN SANDPIPER *Tringa ochropus* (p)

F   2 on Carron at Larbert 16 Feb & 4 on 23rd, last 2 on 12 Mar (MA). 1 Skinflats 27 Jun & 9 Aug (GO). 2 Lathallan 10 Nov (JW).

C   1 Blackdevon Wetlands 16 Apr (CJH).

S   1 on Forth at Kippen 22 Mar & 1 Ashfield on 24th (DR AW). 1 Thornhill 17 Sep (NB). 1 Lecropt 20 Oct & 21 Dec (DT).

COMMON SANDPIPER *Tringa hypoleucos* (B)

Spring return in April: 4th at Doune, 18th Killin, 20th Kinbuck & Alva, 21st Blairdrummond, 23rd Cromlix & Carron Valley Res (DOE PWS MVB AT NB DT).

F   Skinflats: lst of autumn 6 Jul, max 3 from 18 Jul to 9 Aug. Kinneil from 6 Jul to 18 Sep, max 9 on 15 Aug (GO DT).

C   8 Alloa Inch 30 Jul (RJD).

S   3 G.Finglas 18 May (DAC).

Passage autumn totals :

	Jul	Aug	Sep
	11 15	13 8	10 1

TURNSTONE *Arenaria interpres* (W)

F   2 Kinneil 17 Aug & 3 on 25th. 1 Skinflats 21Aug. 7 Bo'ness 20 Oct (DT GO DMB). At Blackness from 27 Jan, max 30 on 24 Mar, last 10 on 21 Apr. 12 on 22 Sep (MA).

*POMARINE SKUA *Stercorarius pomarinus*

F   1 Ad Bo'ness 8 Sep (DMB).

ARCTIC SKUA *Stercorarius parasiticus* (p)

F   Kinneil: 25 birds from 22 Aug to 28 Sep, max 9 on 9 Sep (DT DMB). 3 Blackness 22 Sep & 1 Juv on 14 Oct – chasing Blackheaded Gulls (MA). 1 Airth 11 Oct, 1 S.Alloa on 12th & 2 on 18th (all Juv, RJD).

C   1 Juv ->E Cambus 4 Nov (RJD).

*GREAT SKUA *Catharacta skua*

F   3 Kinneil 15 Aug &1 on 9 Sep. (DT).

*MEDITERRANEAN GULL *Larus melanocephalus*

2001.C 1 *(first winter) at Gartmorn Dam 29 Sep. Adult in winter plumage on Forth at Alloa Inch 6 Nov and at Fallin on the 20th & 29th (RJD).*

*LITTLE GULL *Larus minutus*

F   Kinneil: 1 Juv 10 Aug, 8 (6 Ad) on 2 Nov & 1 Ad on 9th (DT GO). 1 (1st summer) Pow Burn 21 Aug (RJD).

BLACK-HEADED GULL *Larus ridibundus* (B,W)

F   1st Juv at Skinflats on 28 Jun (GO). 160 S.Alloa 19 Aug & 600 Airth on 21st RJD).

S   170 at Cambusbeg GP colony in Apr & 200 in May (RD). 250 ant-catching at BoA 2 Aug (CJH).

COMMON GULL *Larus canus* (B,W)
F   1st Juv S.Alloa 6 Aug. 160 Gallamuir 8 Nov (RJD). 470 Slamannan 3 Sep (NB).
C   315 Gartmorn 17 Feb (AT).
S   20 L.Tay 26 Feb, 1st of spring; 200 on 12 Mar (PWS). 58 at Cambusbeg GP colony in Apr & 50 in May (RD). 10 Pr L.Ruskie, 1 Pr L.Watston (DOE CJH). 360 L.Coulter 3 Dec & 1270 Lake of Menteith on 15th (NB).

LESSER BLACK-BACKED GULL *Larus fuscus* (b,S)
        Eight Jan records (15 birds) & 4 in Dec. Spring arrival: 36 Skinflats 7 Mar & 74 L.Ellrig on 29th (DT JN).
        No breeding records, though nesting presumably still occurs on several rooftops.
F   3 Kinneil 1 Jan. (MA). 77 Skinflats 29 Aug, 25 S.Alloa 10 Oct; still 34 L.Coulter 5 Nov (NB RJD HC).
S   1 Carron Valley Res 13 Jan & from 14 Sep to 21 Dec (DAC).

HERRING GULL *Larus argentatus* (b,S,W)
F   5000 Kinneil 6 Jan. Roost flight over Kincardine Bridge 18 Dec ended at 16.15 (DT CJH). 800 Slamannan 9 Jan (NB).
C   900 Alloa tip 27 Jan & 800 on 13 Dec. 3500 on roost flight at Blackdevonmouth on 31 Dec (CJH). 3000 Cambus 4 Nov (NB).

*ICELAND GULL *Larus glaucoides*
S   1 (1st winter) Fallin on 30 Mar. A probable 1st summer bird seen here on 5 Aug, possibly Glaucous Gull (RJD HC). *2001: At least 2 Ad & 2 lst W at Fallin/Polmaise 11 Jan to 7 Apr; 1 Ad 16 Dec (RJD).*

*GLAUCOUS GULL *Larus hyperboreus*
S/F   1 (1st winter) 21 Mar (GO). 1 Fallin 2 Nov, 1 Cambus on 5th & 1 Higgins Neuk on 8th, all adults – first and last record certainly same bird (wing damage) (RJD NB). *2001: 1 Ad & 2 1st W at Fallin 1 Jan to 22 Apr (RJD).*

GREAT BLACK-BACKED GULL *Larus marinus* (S,W)
F   125 Kinneil 1 Jan (MA).
S   28 (Ad) Skinflats 13 Oct (GO). Fallin Tip: 30 on 26 Jan; 113 on 17 Nov & 210 on 28 Dec (286 Ad, ie 89% Ad). Inland records: 11 L.Ellrig 6 Oct (JN). 2 Carron Valley Res 2 Dec (RJD HC). 1 L.Dochard 9 Dec (NB).

KITTIWAKE *Rissa tridactyla* (P,w)
F   At Kinneil: 5 on 5 Jul, 30 on 13 Sep, 230 on 2 Nov (DT GO). 1 Blackness 24 Feb (MA).
S   1 imm ->W at L.Dochart 9 Feb (DT). *Most inland records are from Forth Valley (CJH).*

*CASPIAN TERN *Sterna caspia*
F   1 Adult Skinflats Pools 8 Jul (GO). Photographs of bird, descriptions also by K Shaw & R Shand, record accepted by BBRC. First record for Upper Forth.

Figure 3: Adult Caspian Tern at Skinflats Pools, July 8, 2002. First record for Upper Forth.
Photograph courtesy of G. Owens

SANDWICH TERN *Sterna sandvicensis* (P)
F   Autumn return from 24 Jun, max 350 Kinneil 17 Aug (AT DT). 200 Carriden 8 Sep (DMB). Max above Kincardine Bridge, 15 Pow Burn 1 Sep; last 1 S.Alloa 1 Oct (RJD).
S   Heard over Fallin on 5 dates 21 Jul to 9 Aug (RJD).

COMMON TERN *Sterna hirundo* (B)
F   1st, 1 Skinflats 24 Apr, 49 on 5 May; last 1 Kinneil 2 Nov (GO DT). Furthest up river were single Juvs at S.Alloa 19 Aug & 3 Sep (RJD). 106 nests (birds apparently incubating) at Grangemouth Docks colony on 8 Jun; probably a successful breeding season but numbers reared difficult to judge since colony active till late August (DMB).

*BLACK TERN *Chlidonias niger*
F   1 Kinneil 24 Aug (DT).

GUILLEMOT *Uria aalge* (W)
F   1 Skinflats 1 Jan flew SW over pools & continued inland (MA).
F/S   Considerable influx in autumn from 1 at Kinneil 6 Sep, 11 on 21st & 20 Skinflats + 7 Blackness on 22nd. Then in Oct: 10 S.Alloa on 1st, 22 Fallin on 2nd & 60 S.Alloa on 10th. 7 Cambuskenneth on 23 Nov & 10 Kinneil on 24th; few in Dec (DT DMB MA RJD AT).
S   1 Forthbank 10 Mar (AT). Singles in autumn: Dunblane 21 Sep & Earlsburn Res in 23rd; 1 ->W Lecropt 23 Nov, Lake of Menteith on 24th & Airthrey on 28th (DOE DT MVB NB).

*RAZORBILL *Alca torda*
F   3 Blackness 24 Feb (MA). 1 Bo'ness 8 Sep, 3 Pow Burn 10 Oct & 2 on 11th (DMB RJD).

*PUFFIN *Fratercula arctica*
F   1 Kinneil 21/28 Sep; 2 (1 Ad, 1 1st winter) Pow Burn 11 Oct (DT RJD).

FERAL PIGEON *Columba livia* (B,W)
F   230 Skinflats 8 Sep (MVB).

STOCK DOVE *Columba oenas* (B,W)
    BBS records only in farmland, 1.4 birds 10 km^{-1}.
F   Max Skinflats 26 on 17 Feb, 7 on 1 May. 12 Kinneil 14 Apr (MA AB GO). 20 Camelon 20 Jan, 11 on 7 Apr (MA).
S   50 Lanrick 12 Jan, on Braes of Doune 20 Argaty 17 Jan & Pr nested Coilechat but failed; 50 Lecropt 23 Feb & 10 Thornhill 13 Mar. 40 Gallamuir 5 Dec. (DOE DC DT RJD).

WOODPIGEON *Columba palumbus* (B,W)
    Greatly under-reported. BBS shows 5.9 birds 10 km^{-1} in farmland, 2x more than in urban or conifer habitats. No trend since 1996.
S   350 Dunblane 11 Mar, 500 Lecropt 21 Apr; 110 Gallamuir 13 Nov (DC DT RJD).

COLLARED DOVE *Streptopelia decaocto* (B,W)
    Greatly under-reported. Scarce away from suburbs and large farms. BBS shows 14.5 birds 10 km^{-1} in suburbs, frequency now only half that of longterm average.
C   Singing Tillicoultry 23 Dec (AT).
    7 Killin 1 Jan & 2 on 16 Oct (PWS). 23 E.Row 13 Jan & 31 Lecropt 24 Feb (MVB). 20 Cambuskenneth 23 Nov (AT).

CUCKOO *Cuculus canorus* (B)
    First record 20 April, Flanders Moss; then in May: Aberfoyle & L.Tay on 1st, G.Lochay on 2nd, Doune on 3rd (DOE BTO PWS). BBS shows mainly in conifers, frequency as 1999 & 2000 but only half that of longterm average.
F   Juv Skinflats 4 Jul (GO).

1 Braes of Doune 10 Aug (DOE).
BARN OWL   *Tyto alba* (b,w)
S   Reported in Mar/Apr at Kippen, Braes of Doune (W.Coilechat), Cambusmore (dead), L.Venachar (road death, 1st W F, ringed 3 Jul 2001 by M Steward, 5 km S near Port of Menteith); In autumn at Ashfield, Lecropt, Callander, & Thornhill (DAC DC BC DP DT DMB).
TAWNY OWL   *Strix aluco* (B,W)
Reported in Jan-May at Bo'ness, Tillicoultry, Woodhill, Gartmorn, Strathyre. In autumn additionally at Fallin.. (AS AT DC RJD HC).
*LONG-EARED OWL   *Asio otus* (b,w)
F   1 Skinflats 6 Feb to 23 Apr (GO). 1 (dead by road) Dunmore 1 Sep (RJD HC).
S   1 Bannockburn 19 Jun, young heard Flanders Moss 7 Jul, 1 Ashfield 3 Dec (RJD HC DOE DP).
SHORT-EARED OWL   *Asio flammeus* (b,W)
Remains very local, both in winter and, especially, in potential breeding localities.
F   Kinneil: 5 on 5 Jan & 3 on 19th, 1 on 17 Apr; 1 on 16 Oct. (DAC DT RJD).
C   2 Cambus 30 Apr (AT).
S   1 Sheriffmuir 28 Mar (AT). 1 Gargunnocks (Buckieburn Res) 6 Oct (NB).
SWIFT   *Apus apus* (B)
First records in May and later than usual: 3 Dunblane on 6th, at Dollar on 9th, at Stirling & BoA on 12th, Doune on 13th, Killin (6) on 14th, Denny on 16th & Falkirk on 17th (BTO DT JNW DMB DOE PWS AB). Typical last dates were in Aug – Doune on 14th, BoA on 16th, Bo'ness & Falkirk on 17th, Stirling 21st (DOE CJH DT AB JNW), but 2 Kinneil on 28 Sep were unusual (DT).
F   33 Falkirk 5 Aug (JNW). 20 Kinneil 10 Aug (DT).
S   Max over Doune 34 on 16 Jul & BoA 30 on 13 Jun & 3/6 Aug, but 60 Lecropt 30 Jun & 45 Stirling 10 Aug. (DOE JNW CJH DT).
KINGFISHER   *Alcedo atthis* (b,w)
Recorded throughout but only 6 records Apr to Jul - probably reflects WEBS activity.
F   Pr on Carron below Denny 3 Mar & Ad+2J on 29 May, 1 in Feb & Sep-Dec (MA AS AB). At Kinneil 21 Sep to 24 Dec, max 2 on 29 Oct; 1 Skinflats 24 Feb & 9 Sep to 8 Dec (AB DT GO).
C   At 3 sites on Devon (one with occupied burrow),Tillicoultry-Dollar Feb-Jun & Dec (AT DAC NB GEL). 2 Blackdevonmouth 29 Sep & 1 on 18 Oct; 1 Gartmorn on 14 Jan & 24 Dec, 2 on 19 Oct (CJH AT).
S   On lower Teith 17 Feb & Sep-Nov (DOE MW RJD NB). 1 Airthrey 24 Aug to 24 Oct (MVB).
*WRYNECK   *Jynx torquilla*
F   1 Kinneil 31 Aug (DT).
GREEN WOODPECKER   *Picus viridis* (B,W)
F   1 Denny 3 Mar; 1 Wallacebank Wood 20 Apr & 26 Oct; 1 Dunmore Wood 14 Apr & 1 Sep (MA AS AB RJD).
C   3 sites, Alva Woodland Park to Dollar Glen Mar to May (AT).
S   Singles at Fallin Aug-Dec, Gallamuir Wood 7 Dec, Airthrey Feb/Apr, Dumyat 15 Apr (RJD HC MVB DP). Few reports from west of area: 1 G.Lochay 16 May & 1 Port of Menteith on 27th (CS DOE).
GREAT SPOTTED WOODPECKER   *Dendrocopus major* (B,W)
F   1 Skinflats 14 Jan, 17 Feb & 16 Oct. 1 Dunmore Wood (drumming) 14 Apr (GO AB). 1 Bo'ness, Bonny Water & Wallacebank Wood in Jan, 3 sites Falkirk Mar/Apr & 1 Larbert Dec (AS MA).

C   1 Tillicoultry 7 Jan, 1 Gartmorn 11 May (AT).

S   Reported Jan-May L.Dochart, L.Katrine, Buchlyvie, Arnprior & Flanders Moss; Fallin Jul/Aug, Gallamuir Oct-Dec, Stirling 10 Sep, Carron Valley Res 3 Nov (DAC CS DP RJD HC JNW).

SKYLARK *Alauda arvensis* (B,W)

Singing Lecropt 2 Feb (DT). BBS shows 47 birds 10 km^{-1} on moorland, 11 on farmland, frequency close to longterm average.

F   Song in Apr at Skinflats & Camelon. 50 Skinflats 3 Jan & 70 on 20 Oct (AB AS MVB). 20 Airth 14 Oct (RJD).

C   Singing birds at 15 sites Apr-Jun (AT).

S   100 Fallin 23 Jan; 100 Lecropt 26 Jan, 40 on 20 Oct (RJD DT).

SAND MARTIN *Riparia riparia* (B)

1st records on 26 March at Gartmorn (10) & Lake of Menteith (75, 150 on 30th), 7 Camelon on 30th; then in April: Inverlochlarig on 1st, Airthrey on 4th & Carronshore on 6th, 200 Lake of Menteith on 7th, 1 Skinflats on 8th, 4 Ashfield & 47 Barbush on 10th (AT DT DOE MA MVB AB). Last 28 S.Alloa 19 Aug (RJD).

F   6 over Carron at Camelon 29 May (AS).

S   200 Lecropt 24 Apr, 300 Cambusmore 28 Jun (BTO PWS). 18 nests Inverlochlarig (DOE).

SWALLOW *Hirundo rustica* (B)

1st records in April: Thornhill on 4th, Doune & Callendar on 6th, Carron Valley Res & Airthrey on 13th, widespread from 20th (DOE DAC BTO). Last in late October: Skinflats (6) on 20th, Lecropt on 23rd, Kinneil (7) on 26th, Gallamuir on 31st (MVB DC DT RJD). BBS frequency only 64 % of 2000 but close to longterm average.

C   100 Tullibody Inch roost 20 Aug (MVB).

S   100 Doune on 21 Sep & 30 G.Lochay on 22nd (DOE PWS).

HOUSE MARTIN *Delichon urbica* (B)

Arrivals in April: Blairdrummond on 20th, Carron Valley Res on 23rd & Braes of Doune on 26th (DOE DT DC). No really late dates, 20 Doune on 21 Sep, G.Lochay on 22nd & Stirling on 25th (DOE PWS DT). BBS frequency as 2000, both above longterm average.

S   Nest counts: 20 Inverlochlarig, 10 (at least 7 active) BoA Museum hall, 6 G.Lochay Dunchroisg (DOE CJH PWS). 1 Pr, 1st confirmed breeding, Fallin (RJD). 200 Dunblane 15 Aug (DP).

TREE PIPIT *Anthus trivialis* (B)

First at Flanders Moss 20 Apr (DOE), then Aberfoyle (4) on 28 Apr; 4 G.Lochay on 6 May (DOE DT). Last 1 Fallin 28 Aug (RJD HC). BBS shows 3 per 10 km in conifers, as 2000 but below longterm average.

MEADOW PIPIT *Anthus pratensis* (B,W)

Relatively scarce midwinter: 22 Fallin 28 Dec (RJD). Spring return 17 Dalglen Burn, Tillicoultry, 14 Feb (AT) –*rather early for c350 m (CJH)*. BBS shows 127 birds 10 km^{-1} on moorland, as longterm average.

S   100+60 Kinbuck 29 Sep (MVB).

*ROCK PIPIT *Anthus petrosus*

F   1 Blackness 3 Feb (MA). 2 Bo'ness 20 Oct (DMB). 1 Kinneil 16 Oct & 22 Dec (RJD DT). 2 S.Alloa 1 Oct, 5 Pow Burn 11 Oct (with Meadow Pipits on pasture). 2 Higgins Neuk 8 Nov & 4 on 31 Dec (RJD).

*YELLOW WAGTAIL *Motacilla flava*

F   Adult males, one of race *flavissima* & one of *flava* (Blue-headed) feeding on same dungheap at Skinflats 19 & 21 May (AB GO).

GREY WAGTAIL Motacilla cinerea (B,w)
    Only 2 January records, Killin & Cambus; 5 in February & widespread in March. 6 in December (PWS KW AB MA et al).
F   At 4 sites in Mar/Apr including 2 pairs at Bo'ness away from water (AS). 4 Camelon 16 Feb (MA) – spring arrival? (CJH).
C   At 7 sites Mar-Jun (AT).
S   5 summer sites from Buchlyvie to Balquhidder (DAC). Many sites occupied (HR).
PIED WAGTAIL Motacilla alba (B, w)
    Noted at only 5 sites in Jan (PWS AT DAC). BBS shows 8 birds 10 km^{-1} on farmland, 4 in suburban & 2 on moorland; as longterm average.
F   White Wagtail M.a.alba: 2 Skinflats 27 Apr & 3 on 29th (GO).
    White Wagtail M.a.alba: 2 G.Buckie 29 Mar – unusual locality & rather early for this (Icelandic?) migrant (DT).
*WAXWING Bombycilla garrulus
S   1 Stirling 5 Jan (BS).
DIPPER Cinclus cinclus (B,W).
C   14 on Devon, Tillicoultry-Dollar, in Mar; 13 in Dec (DE). 1 Gartmorn Dam 16 Nov (AT).
S   6 on Teith at Lanrick 6 Jan & 5 on 22 Dec (DOE). In song at Airthrey 5 Feb (MVB), but few reports from breeding areas.
WREN Troglodytes troglodytes (B,W)
    Widespread and common, few records, Ed. BBS shows 59 birds 10 km^{-1} on farmland, 33 in suburban, 5 in conifers & 3 on moorland; slightly above longterm average.
HEDGE SPARROW Accentor modularis (B,W)
    BBS shows 7 birds/10 km on farmland, 12 in suburban & 1.3 in conifers; as longterm average.
ROBIN Erithacus rubecula (B,W)
    Under-recorded (CJH). BBS average of 13.5 birds 10 km^{-1} is very close to 2000 average as well as 8-year average; highest density in conifers (21.4), then urban (21.0) and farmland (17.1), none recorded on moorland.
F   1 in Bo'ness garden through Jan, territorial pair late Jan till late Feb (AS). 1 in song at 2 a.m Airth 31 Dec (AT).
REDSTART Phoenicurus phoenicurus (B)
    None recorded in BBS, but generally under-recorded (Ed.) 1st spring: M at Killin 22 Apr (PWS).
S   5 G.Lochay 6 May (DT). 1 AoT Flanders Moss 16 Jun (RJD HC). 39 nests produced 104 Y at Trossachs colony, heavy Pine Marten predation (HR).
WHINCHAT Saxicola rubetra (B)
    BBS average of 0.4 birds 10 km^{-1} (across all habitats) stems from moorland squares only. None recorded from coniferous plantations, which together with Bracken used to be its main habitat 20-30 years ago. The average is the same as the 2000 average but only a third of the 8-year average.
C   1 above Dollar Glen 26 May (AT). 1 J Myreton Hill 21 Jul (MA).
S   Recorded in summer at Inverlochlarig, Glen Finglas, Flanders Moss. Last Sheriffmuir 21 Sep (DT DAC RJD HC MVB).
STONECHAT Saxicola torquata (b,w)
    BBS average of 0.6 birds 10 km^{-1} stems from moorland squares only. This is 3 times the 2000 average as well as 3 times the 8-year average and the highest density recorded so far. This may well be indicative of a medium-term recovery from a slump in the 1990s.

F   At Skinflats 6 Jan to 24 Feb, 18 Sep and 20 Dec (GO AB MVB). Pr east of Kinneil on 19 Jan (DAC)

C   1 Cambus 4 /15 Nov (RJD). 1 G.Quey 24 Nov (MVB).

S   In breeding season pairs noted at Balquhidder (G.Dubh), Flanders Moss, Sheriffmuir (2), Gargunnocks (Cringate) (DT RJD HC CS CJH). 11 Kippen Muir 20 Sep, wintered Lecropt Feb & Oct/Nov; 1 CocksBurn Res 24 Feb (DT AT).

WHEATEAR *Oenanthe oenanthe* (B)

     BBS average of 1.4 birds 10 km^{-1} (across all habitats) stems from moorland only. Up 75 % on the 2000 average and up 27 % on 8-year average.

     1st of spring: 3 Stronend 25 Mar, 2 at Glen Buckie 29 Mar, 1 at G. Kendrum and 2 at Ballochleam (Gargunnock Hills) on 30 Mar (DT, DC, DAC).

F   2 migrants Kinneil 4 Aug (DT, GO); 3 on 21 Aug and single on 31 Aug at Skinflats (GO).

C   2 M near The Law (Ochils) 13 Apr (AT).

     1 at Carse of Lecropt 21 Apr (DT).

*RING OUZEL *Turdus torquatus* (b)

S   1 G.Kendrum 11 Apr & 1 Monachyle Glen on 18th (JHA). M at G. Dubh 28 May (DC)

BLACKBIRD *Turdus merula* (B,W)

     BBS average of 25.4 birds 10 km^{-1} is same as in 2000 and down 11 % on 8-year average. Blackbird density is highest in the Urban habitat (106.6 birds 10 km^{-1}), where it is more than 3 times as frequent as on farmland, 30 times as frequent as in coniferous woodland. The density on moorland (0.4 birds 10 km^{-1}) is insignificant.

C   10 Aitkenhead (Forest Mill) 7 Jan; 1 nest in tractor Gartmorn 11 May; unusual assemblage of 11 at Tillicoultry 18 May (AT).

S   1 singing at dusk at Airthrey on 31 Jan, 20 in BoA garden 11 Oct and an exceptional 54, mainly juvs., feeding in a hedgerow in Bannockburn 30 Jul (CJH DC).

FIELDFARE *Turdus pilaris* (W)

     Spring departure: 180 Avonbridge 8 Apr, 9 Gartmorn Dam 17 Apr (AT).

     1st of autumn was 1 ->W Dunblane 6 Oct (MVB) with the main arrival from 18 Oct, the first sizeable flocks being 75 at Carse of Lecropt 20 Oct and 100 on 29 Oct (DT RJD).

F   40 Kinneil 6 Jan and 100 -> W Skinflats 19 Oct were largest reported flocks (DT AB).

C   70 Gartmorn Dam 14 Jan (AT); 215 ->W at Fallin 3 Nov & 210 Haugh of Blackgrange on 4th (RJD).

S   flocks of up to 200 Carse of Lecropt in late Jan and late Feb (DT MVB); 69 Stirling 19 Jan, 2 flocks totalling 103 Blairlogie 6 Feb, 140 West Cambushinnie 16 Feb & 180 Ashfield 14 Apr (AT CJH MVB); several reports of flocks in excess of 100 from the Carse of Lecropt area during the first two weeks of November, the largest being 550 on 3 Nov (MVB); 215 at Fallin 3 Nov -> W and 50 there 11 Nov (RC).

SONG THRUSH *Turdus philomelos* (B,W)

     BBS average of 6.2 birds 10 km^{-1} is 25 % down on 2000 average and 7 % on 8-year average. Song Thrush density is highest in (sub)urban (14.5 birds 10 km^{-1}), followed by conifers (10.4), farmland (6.8) and moorland (0.4)

     Few in January: 5 Fallin on 3rd, 1 Doune & at 5 sites around Falkirk (RJD MA AS DAC). First song noted 30 Jan to 17 Feb. Roost of at least 4 birds at Woodland Park, Alva 9 Feb (AT RJD).

F   At 13 sites Feb to June (AS). 20+ Skinflats 3 and 19 Oct, up to 7 feeding on Yew berries in Bo'ness garden between 11 and 21 Oct and 5 at South Alloa 23 Oct (AB AS RJD).

C   6 Gartmorn Dam 15 Sep (RJD).

S   8 BoA garden 11 Oct (CJH).

REDWING *Turdus iliacus* (W)

Last of spring were 100 at Upper Lanrick on 4 Apr and 50 at Ashfield 14 Apr (DT MVB).

First of autumn were comparatively late with 2 at Fallin on 2 Oct with the main arrival from 8th. No very large flocks were reported.

F   Largest flocks were 40 at Fallin, 50 at Blackness and ca. 150 with other thrushes at Skinflats both on 19 Oct (RJD DAC AB).

C   70+ in Tillicoultry on 7 Jan and 133 at Marchglen on 26th (AT).

S   Largest winter flocks were 75 on the Carse of Lecropt 23 Feb & 100 on 3 Nov (DT MVB). Autumn flocks included 79 in Dunblane on 8 Oct, 50 in BoA on 11th, 150 Thornhill Carse10 Nov & 70 Braes of Doune 15 Dec (CJH RJD MVB).

MISTLE THRUSH *Turdus viscivorus* (B,W)

Greatly under-recorded. BBS average of 1.3 birds 10 km^{-1} is up 44 % on 2000 average and up 18 % on 8-year average. This is the second highest density after the 1998 high of 2.3. The species is most abundant on moorland (2.9), followed by conifers (1.3) and farmland (0.6).

F   4 Carronshore 6 Oct; 6 at South Alloa 10 Oct. 3 in Bo'ness garden in mixed thrush flock stripped yew tree of berries between 21st and 27th Oct (AB RJD AS). Singles at Skinflats Jan/Feb and Oct (GO AB).

12 Buchlyvie 3 Mar & 1 Plean CP on 9th (DAC AB)

GRASSHOPPER WARBLER *Locustella naevia* (b)

F   1 sg at Skinflats 14 Apr to 1 May (AB GO). 1 Kinneil 31 May (DT).

C   AoTs at Marchglen and Cambus Pools (AT).

S   In song at Flanders Moss 20 Apr, L. Ruskie 7 May (2) and Invertrossachs 30 Jun (DOE).

SEDGE WARBLER *Acrocephalus schoenobaenus* (B)

BBS average (0.9 birds 10 km) across all habitats derives from farmland squares only. It is only a third of 2000 average, which was the highest recorded, and down 25 % on 8-year average.

1st of spring: 2 Blairdrummond 25 Apr, 1 Kinneil 3 May, 1 L. Ruskie 9 May, 2 L.Tay, Killin 16 May. More widespread from 20 May onwards. Last reported of autumn: 2 Y at Fallin 10 Aug were presumed migrants (DOE DT PWS RJD).

F   1 Kinneil 3 May; 4 singing Skinflats 20 May (DT AB).

C   3 singing at Cambus Pools 1 Jun (CJH).

S   5 singing Blairdrummond 26 May, 4 Balquhidder (Balvag) 27 May, 1 L. Watston 28 May, 1 Blackwater Marshes 16 Jul (DOE CJH).

WHITETHROAT *Sylvia communis* (B)

BBS average (2.5 birds 10 km^{-1}), though down 22 % on 2000 average, is up 36 % on 8-year average, being the second highest figure. It remains to be seen whether this represents an upwards trend for the species. The species is most abundant in "urban" squares (6.6 birds 10 km^{-1}), followed by farmland (4.0), none elsewhere.

1st records in spring: 1 Skinflats 25 Apr. In May: 1 at Skinflats on 1st; 1 singing on R. Devon at Alva on 2nd; 1 River Carron at Carronshore on 2nd, Flanders Moss 4th, Doune 6th. Last: 1 Airth on 13 Sep, 1 Skinflats 22 Sep (GO CJH AB DOE RJD AB).

F   1 Camelon 29 May; 2 prs. West Mains, Falkirk 19 Jun. 1 singing Fallin 28 Jun was down on previous year; 2 carrying food at South Alloa 30 Jul (AS RJD).

C   2 R. Devon, W of Dollar, on 9 May; 1 Cambus Pools 1 Jun (DT CJH).

GARDEN WARBLER *Sylvia borin* (B)

     1st records, usually singing, in May: 1 BoA 2nd, 1 AoT Polmont from 4th, 1 Devon W of Dollar 9th, 1 Doune 10th, 1 Lake of Menteith 11th (DMB DT JW DOE RB). Last of autumn: 2 feeding on Elder at Skinflats 22 Sep (AB)

F   1 on Canal at Grangemouth 19 Jun (AS).

BLACKCAP *Sylvia atricapilla* (B)

     The average of 1.7 birds 10 km^{-1} is almost twice that of 2000 (0.9), up 54 % on the 8-year average and represents the second highest recorded. Only recorded on farmland (3.0) and conifers (1.3).

     Winter records: M & F BoA garden 27 Jan; 2M & 1F on 3 Mar, F there 15 Dec (*possibly returning bird ? Ed.*). M feeding on apples in Stirling garden on 7 Feb (MVB JNW). F at Polmont on 23 Nov; M in Bo'ness garden from 9 to 22 Dec (JW AS). Spring arrival in April, started with a M at Camelon on 6th, then singing birds at Fallin on 20th , BoA & Stirling (2) on 23rd, 2 Blairdrummond on 25th , 1 at Doune Lodge & 2 Airthrey on 26th, then F at Bo'ness on 28th (MA RJD CJH DOE AS).

F   Singing bird Fallin 28 Jun was different from spring site. M singing at Skinflats 5 Jul repeats last year's presence at this unusual site, followed by a f/imm on 9 Aug (RJD GO).

S   Singing bird L.Watston 28 May. Ad + 2 Y Plean CP 14 Jul (MVB CJH AB).

WOOD WARBLER *Phylloscopus sibilatrix* (B)

     Under-recorded. Spring arrival: Singing birds G. Finglas 28 Apr, then L. Voil 5 May & 5 G. Lochay & 13 Loch Katrine on 6th (DOE DT BTO).

C   2 singing Dollar Glen 26 May (AT).

CHIFFCHAFF *Phylloscopus collybita* (B)

     Scarce on BBS squares, especially compared to Willow Warbler, which is 57 times as frequent. Down a fifth on 2000, the average (0.4 birds 10 km^{-1}) is exactly the same as the 8-year average.

     Spring arrival in March: Singing birds BoA 24th, Blairdrummond 25th, Woodland Park Alva in same spot as last two years 26th, Stirling Castle & G. Finglas 28th, Broomridge Stirling 29th, & Larbert on 30th. Widespread in early April. (DMB DOE AT DT MA). Last of autumn: 1 in Fallin garden 29 Sep (RJD); a late individual associating with a mixed Tit flock at Carronshore 6 Oct was possibly the same bird as one on 2 Dec. 1 at Union Canal, Polmont, 8 Dec (AB JW).

F   Song at Larbert Pond 6 Apr (AB). 2 Fallin 7 Apr, 3 by 20 Apr (RJD).

S   Song heard Airthrey, Stirling Castle & Ashfield in first part of April (DMB CJH MVB).

WILLOW WARBLER *Phylloscopus trochilus* (B)

     The BBS average of 19.3 birds 10 km^{-1} is slightly up on the 2000 figure and 15 % down on the 8-year average. It is most abundant in coniferous woodland (53.9), followed by "urban" (21.1), farmland (16.5) and moorland (3.9).

     April arrival: Song at Skinflats & Camelon on 6th, L.Watston and Fallin on 7th, Grangemouth on 10th (2), Doune Ponds 11th. Widespread from mid-month (AB MA DOE RJD AT).

S   Singing birds at North Third Reservoir 16 Apr, BoA 18 Apr, Airthrey 28 Apr. 1-2 birds seen weekly in Stirling garden throughout most of July and August (JNW DMB RJ).

GOLDCREST *Regulus regulus* (B,W)

     Under-recorded (Ed). BBS average (4.1 birds 10 km^{-1}) is up a fifth on both the 2000 and the 8-year average. It is 30 times as abundant in conifers (24.0) as on farmland (0.8).

F   5 Skinflats 11 Jan. In Bo'ness garden 15 Feb & 29 Nov (GO, AS)
In Stirling garden Feb, Mar, Aug, Sep & Nov (RJ).

SPOTTED FLYCATCHER Muscicapa striata (B)
Seems scarce – only 11 reports received yet the BBS average of 1.2 birds
10 km^{-1} is 3 times that of both the 2000 and the 8-year density. Most abundant
on farmland (2.2), 0.6 in conifers; not recorded in the other habitats.
1st spring records in May: Strathyre on 20th , Killin on 22nd, Inverlochlarig on
23rd (the only one seen in the area), Dollar Glen on 26th (DC DT AT). Autumn
passage: 1 Gartmorn Dam 15 Sep (RJD).

S   5 pr G. Lochay 3 Jun. At 8 other sites Killin to Buchlyvie. (DT DAC DOE PWS)

*PIED FLYCATCHER Ficedula hypoleuca (b)
S   20 nests produced 34 Y at Trossachs colony, heavy Pine Marten predation (HR).

LONG-TAILED TIT Aegithalos caudatus (B,W)
BBS average (2 birds 10 km^{-1}) is more than twice that of 2000 and slightly (15 %)
up on 8-year average. Two and a half times as frequent on farmland (3.4) as in
both coniferous and urban habitats (1.3).

F   14 Fallin 7 Sep & 19 on 3 Dec. 9 Skinflats 2 Oct, up to 14 in Bo'ness garden in
second half of Dec (RJD GO AS). 30 by R.Carron at Larbert 15 Dec (MA).

C   11 Cambus 15 Nov (CJH).
10 Airthrey 14 Oct, 18 Argaty, Braes of Doune, 18 Dec (CJH DC).

COAL TIT Parus ater (B,W)
Widespread but under-recorded (Ed.). BBS average (10 birds 10 km^{-1}) is twice
that of the 2000 season and up 45 % on 8-year average. 10 times as frequent in
conifers (49.4) as on farmland (4.8).

BLUE TIT Parus caeruleus (B,W)
Under-recorded (Ed.). BBS average of 19.2 birds 10 km^{-1} is highest recorded so
far. Up 60 % on 2000 average and up 35 % on 8-year average. Most frequent on
farmland (34.1), followed by urban (19.7) and coniferous woodland (3.2) with
none recorded on moorland.

F   Pair & 3 Y Fallin 5 Jun, 20 there 7 Sep (RJD).

C   Repeatedly entered nest box in Dollar Glen 26 May (AT).
1st fledgling seen BoA 11 Jun. 77 Y fledged from 9 nestboxes G. Finglas (CJH
DC).

GREAT TIT Parus major (B,W)
Under-recorded (Ed.). BBS average (6.7 birds 10 km^{-1}) is up 63 % on 2000
average (4.1) but close to 8-year average. Most frequent on farmland (10.5)
followed by urban (6.6) and coniferous woodland (5.8).

F   10 Fallin 13 Oct (RD).

S   1st fledgling seen BoA 12 Jun (CJH). 65 Y fledged from 7 nestboxes Glen Finglas,
including brood of 12 on 17 Jun (DC).

TREECREEPER Certhia familiaris (B,W)
Under-recorded (Ed.). Scarce on BBS squares & only recorded on farmland (1.0),
the same as the 8-year average.

F   Up to 2 birds in Bo'ness garden seen between late Oct and early Dec (AS).

JAY Garrulus glandarius (B,W)
Scarce in BBS squares with an average of 0.5 birds 10 km^{-1}, the same as the 8-
year average. Twice as frequent in coniferous woodland (1.3) as on farmland
(0.6).

F   On 3 Mar, 3+2 Denny & 2 Larbert (MA). Singles Dunmore Woods 14 Apr & 19
May, Blackness 19 Oct (AB DAC).

C Singles Dollar Glen, burn in open landscape, 26 May; Dollarbeg 3 Aug; Pond Wood (Alloa) 13 Nov; Forestmill 31 Dec (AT RJD).

S 2 nr. Aberfoyle 20 Jan was only Trossachs record! Singles N of Buchlyvie 3 May & BoA 21 Sep; Fallin 28 Aug, Gallamuir Wood (Cowie) 24 Oct & 2 there 31 Oct (DAC RJD).

MAGPIE *Pica pica* (B,W)

Abundance around Stirling is not usually noted in the west, large groups now widespread in Falkirk (CJH). BBS average (5.2 birds 10 km^{-1}) is down 9 % on 2000 average and down 15 % on 8-year average. The species does not seem to have recovered from its high during 1994-96 (average 7.4). Ten time as frequent in the urban habitat (42.1) as on farmland (4.0).

F 17 Skinflats 21 Jan (AS). By R.Carron: 27 at Carron 20 Jan & 18 at Camelon 11 Feb (MA).

S 1 Killin 21 Mar & 1 Crianlarich 5 Nov: first records for G.Dochart (PWS RSPB).

JACKDAW *Corvus monedula* (B,W)

An overlooked species, only 6 reports (Ed). BBS shows that the species continues its slow but steady rise since 1994. The 2002 average of 26.5 birds 10 km^{-1} was 80 % higher than in 1994. Most abundant in urban settings (71.0), followed by farmland (40.7), few on moorland (2.1).

C 150 Blackdevonmouth 31 Dec (CJH).

S 48 Plean CP 25 Mar may represent local breeding population. 430 Lecropt headed for Craigforth (roost?) 14 Dec (DT). 170 Camelon 26 Dec (MA).

ROOK *Corvus frugilegus* (B,W)

BBS shows that species continues a trough & peak pattern with the 2002 average of 59.9 birds 10 km^{-1} up 73 % on the 2000 average and up 23 % on the 8-year average. Most abundant on farmland (77.4), then moorland (62.1) and urban (46.1).

F Rookery of 35 on Forth & Clyde Canal, Falkirk (AS).

Small rookery at Malling, Lake of Menteith 19 Apr (RB). Large roost flight at dusk, BoA, as early as 18 Jun (CJH).

CARRION CROW *Corvus corone* (B,W)

Continues its large-scale yearly fluctuations. BS average of 29.8 birds 10 km^{-1} is two thirds down on 2000 average and 21 % on 8-year average. Most common on farmland (49.0) and in urban settings (28.9) with much smaller densities recorded from moorland (8.9) and coniferous woodland (2.6).

C 35 Haugh of Blackgrange 4 Jan were probably same as 40 Cambus Pool 30 Jan (RJD CJH).

S 2 Airthrey 2 Jul ant-bathed, dabbed & scratched (CJH).

HOODED CROW *Corvus cornix* (b, w)

Newly split from Carrion Crow. Remains very scarce on BBS squares (0.2 birds 10 km^{-1}).

S 1 Carse of Lecropt 20 Oct was S of usual range (DT).

RAVEN *Corvus corax* (B,W)

Very scarce on BBS squares (0.3 birds 10 km^{-1}) but fairly stable since 1996.

S/C 13 territories checked, 11 pairs. 5 successful pairs of which 2 raised 7 Y (PSA).

C 1 Birkhill 31 Dec was an unusual location (RJD).

23 at roost, Braes of Doune, 7 Apr & 30 Nov (DOE). 7 Aberfoyle 5 Sep & 5 Sheriffmuir 5 Oct (DC MVB). Outwith of main breeding areas: 2 -> SE Lecropt 7 Sep, 8 Thornhill Carse 2 Sep (DT DC).

STARLING *Sturnus vulgaris* (B,W)

Greatly under-reported (CJH). BS average (45.8 birds 10 km^{-1}) was second lowest. Down 58 % on 2000 average – the highest recorded so far – and 30 % on

8-year average. More than twice as frequent in an urban setting (146.1) as on farmland (66.5) with a few on moorland (4.3).

F   None at Kincardine Bridge roost 18 Dec (CJH).

C   2500 Tullibody Inch 20 Aug (MVB).
Roost of 250 at S mid-Frew, Thornhill Carse, 13 Nov (DC).

ROSY STARLING *Sturnus roseus*

S   1 Gartmore 5 & 7 Aug. On August 5th Mrs E Craig saw a striking bird with a small flock of common starlings feeding on breadcrumbs on her lawn, it was seen again later and also once on 7th, when it was also seen by Mr M Craig; on each occasion it was in sight for several minutes and seen as close as 4 feet, without binoculars. The bird was about the same size as a common starling, with black head and bib, wings, and tail but instantly noticeable because of the rest of plumage – all the rest of the underparts and all the back down to the rump (seen when the bird flew) were pink, as the colour of fresh salmon. No written notes were made but the bird was compared with an account in a small guide and identified as a Rosy Starling . On the 6th J Mitchell visited the garden and failed to see the bird but was entirely convinced of the correctness of the identification.

This is the first record for the area, it occurred during a late summer invasion, mainly of adult birds, which was noted over much of Scotland.

HOUSE SPARROW *Passer domesticus* (B,W)

Under-recorded (Ed). The 2000 BBS return to 1994-96 levels was short-lived: the 2002 average is down 23 % and 13 % down on the 8-year average. Most abundant in the urban category (46.1) followed by farmland (24.8).

F   20 in Fallin garden 25 May, 30 there on 22 Jun & 41 on 6 Jul (RJD).

C   Nests at Gartmornhill Farm on top of lorry 11 May (AT).

S   150 at Thornhill Carse feeding site 5 Jan. 206 Bannockburn 30 Jul, 25 Killin 16 Aug, 120 Thornhill Carse 10 Nov (DC PWS MVB).

TREE SPARROW *Passer montanus* (B,W)

Widely reported in small numbers from Thornhill eastwards. Not recorded on any BBS squares in 2002.

F   16 Camelon 13 Jan. 8 Kinneil 10 Nov, also noted Skinflats, Blackness & Carron/Bonny Water (MA AB).

S   Bred Fallin: Ad. & Y 13 Jun, 9 (mainly Y) there on 28th; 12 on 6 Dec. 8 Gallamuir Farm (Cowie) 31 Oct (RJD). 34 at Cambuskenneth Farm 10 Mar (AT). 69 at Thornhill Carse feeding site 5 Jan, 40 there, including one hybrid bird, on 3 Oct; 3 fledged from nestbox 1 Jul (DC). 100+ at Carse of Lecropt 8 Sep & 30 on 4 Nov (DT DMB).

CHAFFINCH *Fringilla coelebs* (B,W)

BBS average (39.7 birds 10 km[-1]) as 2000; 7 % down on 8-year average. Prominent on farmland (59.1) and conifers (52.6), but scarcer in urban habitats (13.2) and on moorland (2.9).

F   1st Juv at Fallin 14 Jun (RJD).

S   400 Carse of Lecropt 5 Jan & 200 on 24 Feb. 400 Kinbuck 24 Feb & 600 on 29 Sep; 500 Argaty, Braes of Doune 9 Nov. 500 Thornhill-Doune 6 Jan. 300 Dunblane 10 Nov (DT DOE DC DAC MVB).

BRAMBLING *Fringilla montifringilla* (W)

Large group in Doune area in early winter, small autumn return from 19 Oct.

C   5 Woodland Park, Alva 6 Apr (AT).

S   90 Thornhill 23 Jan. 200 Doune 5 Jan & 35 on 18 Mar, last 30 on 11 Apr & 15 Ashfield on 14th. 10 Argaty, Braes of Doune, 9 Mar, 2 there 9 Nov & 6 on 15 Dec. (RJD DOE MVB et al).

GREENFINCH *Carduelis chloris* (B,W)

    Under-recorded. BBS records 33 birds 10 km^{-1} in urban & 12 in farmland, overall just below 8 year average.

F   90+ Skinflats 23 Aug, 170 Airth 13 Sep, 80 South Alloa 1 Oct & 70 there 23 Oct (AT RJD).

C   23 Woodland Park, Alva 3 Mar. 17 in Dollar garden 23 Dec (AT).

S   49 Dunblane 3 Feb. 100 Carse of Lecropt 6 Aug, 38 Strathyre 21 Oct (MVB DT DC).

2001:   *250 Gartmorn Dam 29 Sep (RJD).*

GOLDFINCH *Carduelis carduelis* (B,W)

    BBS records mainly in urban, 8 birds 10 km^{-1}, & 5 in farmland; best year ever – 65 % above 8 year average.

F   30 South Alloa 3 Sep. 35 Kinneil 9/21 Sep. 60 Pow Burn 15 Dec (RD DT MVB).

S   30 Lanrick, Braes of Doune 6 Jan; 30 Argaty, Braes of Doune, 12 Jan & 40 on 2 Mar; 30 Kinbuck 9 Mar; 40 Doune 4 Sep (DOE).

SISKIN *Carduelis spinus* (B,W)

    BBS shows mainly in conifers, 23 birds 10 km^{-1}, & 2 in farmland; the huge annual fluctuations continue with an almost fivefold increase over 2000 to reach 42 % above 8 year average. One garden record from Stirling, as in 2001, plus one from Fallin.

F   50 Falkirk 12 Jan. 27 Jupiter, Grangemouth 3 Dec (MA AT).

C   32 Gartmorn Dam 17 Feb & 37+ there on 24 Dec; 30 Hillfoot Hill 5 Dec; 15 Forestmill 31 Dec (AT RJD).

S   Small groups of up to 5 birds seen weekly in Stirling garden from 8 Jan till mid-April (RJ). 20 Fallin Bing 3 Jan; 20 Loch Ard 31 Jan & 50 Lake of Menteith 19 Mar; 30 BoA 29 Sep to 16 Oct, 35 Kinbuck 29 Sep, 80 Airthrey 23 Oct & 70 Blairdrummond on 30th (RJD DOE CJH DMB MVB).

LINNET *Carduelis cannabina* (B,W)

    BBS shows mainly on moorland, 6 birds 10 km^{-1}, & 4 in farmland. Overall similar to 8 year average.

    Lecropt & Skinflats flocks smaller than in 2001; Doune flocks larger.

F   400 Skinflats 10 Feb & 150 on 24th ; 200 on 20 Oct (MVB AB).

S   250 Argaty, Braes of Doune, 17 Jan. 100 Lanrick 12 Jan. 500 Thornhill Carse 11 Feb, 250 Doune 9 Mar & 100 on 23rd. 150 Stirling & 2 flocks totalling 180 Dunblane on 10 Nov. 120 Cowie 11 Nov & 80 on 1 Dec (DO DC MVB RJD).

TWITE *Carduelis flavirostris* (b,W) S

    Falkirk flocks larger than in 2001.

    35 in Linnet flock Skinflats 3 Jan, 150 on 10 Feb & ca. 100 on 1 Dec. 30 Pow Burn 13 Jan & 300 there 15 Dec. 50 Higgins Neuk 8 Nov & 60 there 31 Dec (AB DT MVB RJD GO).

S   30 Loch Katrine 15 Jan; 20 Argaty, Braes of Doune. 100 Thornhill Carse 4 Feb. Pairs at Severie, Braes of Doune 7 Apr & Inverlochlarig, Balquhidder, 5 May. 2 Killin 4 May & 2 sites G. Lochay in Jun (CS DC DOE PWS).

REDPOLL *Carduelis cabaret* (b,W)

    BBS shows only in conifers, 1.3 birds 10 km^{-1}; a poor year and well below 8 year average. Scarce in winter in Falkirk and Clacks, max 15 Bo'ness 24 Feb (MA).

S   35 Flanders Moss 15 Jan & 11 in Stirling garden feeding on Birch seeds on 17th. 15 Carron Valley Res 2 Mar & 20 on 21 Dec. 25 Callander 11 Apr & 100 Cromlix on 30th. 16 Killin 16 Oct & 12 on 1 Dec. Pr G. Finglas 28 Apr, also at G.Lochay 26 Jun & Gargunnock Hills 18 Jul. (RJD JNW DAC DOE DC PWS CJH).

2001:   *30 Fallin 2 Nov (RJD).*

COMMON CROSSBILL   *Loxia curvirostra* (b,W)
Much larger flocks recorded in Trossachs than in 2001 and visible passage seen in summer in east Stirling.

C   4 Dollar 5 Dec, tape recorded. 1 Forestmill 31 Dec (RJD)
S   25 Carron Valley Res (on Alder) 13 Jan. Flocks on Cairnoch Hill (Carron Valley) reached 70 on 31 Jan & 90 on 16 Feb. 20 Flanders Moss 15 Jan. 130 Braes of Doune 7 Feb, up to 20 Mar/May & smaller flocks also in Trossachs Jan/Feb. 37 Cromlix, 11 Lake of Menteith and 12 Thornhill in April.
10→ E Fallin 7 Jun & 81-> W in small groups 28 Aug. 40 Cardross Moss 29 Oct, 28 Loch Ard Forest 25 Nov, 20 Gart 6 Dec. Small flocks widespread in autumn (RJD HC DAC DOE DC NB DT).
2001:   50 Carron Valley Res 4 Oct (RJD).

*COMMON ROSEFINCH   *Carpodacus erythrinus*
S   Ad M singing close to houses at Auchessan, G.Dochart, 7 Jul; an elusive bird but one view allowed description (A R & S K Armstrong). *Another example of a territorial but unmated male in a northern glen but close to human activity (CJH).*

BULLFINCH   *Pyrrhula pyrrhula* (B,W)
BBS shows only in farmland, 0.8 birds 10 km⁻¹, little change since 1999 but overall 64 % down on 8 year average. *This is very odd since conifers used to be the major habitat but in this habitat there has been a fairly steady decline since 1996 (CJH).*
F   Pairs Bo'ness garden 9 Apr & Dunmore Woods 19 May (AS AB).
S   15 Lanrick 5 Jan. 3M & 4F in Achray Forest 30 Mar (DOE AT). Feeding in Stirling on amelanchier, greengage and Japonica buds in Mar, aquilegia seeds 17 Jul (RJ). Pair Plean CP 14 Jul & Fallin 28 Jun. 4 L.Mahaick 20 Dec (AB RJD).

SNOW BUNTING   *Plectrophenax nivalis* (W)
C   In Ochils, 58 Ben Ever 25 Dec (MA).
20 Sheriffmuir (Dykedale) 12 Jan (RB).

YELLOWHAMMER   *Emberiza citrinella* (B,W)
BBS shows only in farmland, 8.4 birds 10 km⁻¹; overall slightly below 8 year average.
F   2 in Stirling garden 20 & 21 Mar. 6 South Alloa 18 Oct (RJD).
S   120 Thornhill Carse feed site 5 Jan, 50 there on stubble 4 Feb. 20 Doune 5 Jan; 40 Lanrick, Braes of Doune, 6 Jan; 60 Hill of Row, Dunblane, 12 Jan. 2 in gardens Killin & Stirling in Mar (DC DOE PWS RJ).

REED BUNTING   *Emberiza schoeniclus* (B,W)
BBS shows only in moorland, 6 birds 10 km⁻¹, & 3.6 in farmland; sudden increase since 1997-2001, now over twice the 8 year average.
F   6 M West Mains Pond, Falkirk 19 Jun. 13 Kinneil 30 Jul (AB GO).
C   7 Shannockhill Farm, Coalsnaughton 7 Jan. 3 singing Cambus Pools 1 Jun. (AT CJH).
S   18 Lecropt 18 Jan. 6 Buchany, Braes of Doune 7 Feb. 3 singing Blackwater Marshes 16 Jul. Family party Stronachlachar, L.Katrine 21 Jul (DT DOE CJH DAC).

ESCAPED SPECIES

RUDDY SHELDUCK   *Tadorna ferruginea*
CORRECTION : The bird seen by AT (which showed no signs of hybridisation) on 16 Sep & 14 Oct, 2001, was on the R.Forth at Cambuskenneth (NOT Gartmorn).

THE FLEAS (SIPHONAPTERA) RECORDED FROM CLACKMANNANSHIRE

R.S. George

Clackmannanshire is the smallest of our counties and, as such, was combined with Perthshire by H.C. Watson in *Cybele Britannica*, 3, pp. 524-528, 1852 and in 1859 volume 4, pp. 139-142, was placed in a division of Perthshire to be known as West Perth, vice-county 87. The current usage and boundary divisions of all the vice-counties are in Dandy, (1969), *Watsonian Vice-Counties of Great Britain, Ray Society*, no. 146, pp. 3-36. Clackmannanshire is not a vice-county in its own right.

I was approached by Craig Macadam, who is preparing a paper on the invertebrates of Clackmannanshire, for flea records and as his effort ties in with my rather interrupted aim, to produce as many county lists of fleas as possible, this short list has been prepared.

In chronological order of publication we get:

(i) From Waterston, (1909):
Ceratophyllus gallinae (Schrank), common at Kennetpans (near Kincardine-on-Forth), 8-10. viii. 1908, *M. lugubris, P. domesticus, P. coeruleus*. A female also among dead leaves at the same place. *C. farreni*, Roths., 9 male 27 female, *C. urbica*, Kennetpans, 10.viii. 1908. *C. hirundinis* (Curtis), male and 9 female, *C. urbica*, Kennetpans, 10.viii. 1908.

(ii) Rothschild, (1952) fills out Waterston's 1909 records from material in the collection of the British Museum (Natural History) – now The Natural History Museum, London – thus:
Ceratophyllus gallinae, 4 male 10 female, *Passer domesticus*, Kennetpans, 8-10.viii. 1908, J. Waterston; 5 male 6 female, *Motacilla alba yarrelli*, Kennetpans, 6.viii.08, J. Waterston; 8 male < female, *Parus coeruleus* nest, 8-10.viii.08, Kennetpans, J. Waterston.

(iii) Smit, (1957), in his immensely useful paper, lists as having seen Clackmannanshire specimens of *Ceratophyllus gallinae, C. rusticus* Wagner, *C.f. farreni, C. hirundinis* and *C. garei* Rothschild but no data is given.

(iv) Thompson, (1958), repeats Waterston's records.

(v) Mead-Briggs and Page, (1964), record:
1 female *Archaeopsylla e.erinacei* (Bouché), 1 male *Nosopsyllus fasciatus* (Bosc) and 4 male 4 female *Spilopsyllus cuniculi* (Dale) from male rabbit, 11.X.62, Harvieston, nr. Dollar. The first two species are stragglers on rabbit, *erinacei* from hedgehog and *fasciatus* from rats. *Spilopsyllus cuniculi* is specific to rabbits but does occur on hares and cats.

(vi) Mead-Briggs, (1964), repeats the above *S. cuniculi* record.

(vii) Usher, (1968), records collecting from mole nests during the previous five years seven species but, unfortunately, the only data he gives are the 10 km squares of the national grid. He collected: *Hystrichopsylla t.talpae* (Curtis), NS99; *Rhadinopsylla pentacantha* (Rothschild), NS99; *Palaeopsylla kohauti* Dampf, NS99; *Palaeopsylla minor* (Dale), NS99; *Ctenophthalmus n.nobilis* (Rothschild), NS99, NT09; *Ct. n.vulgaris* Smit, NS99, NT09; *Ct. bisoctodentatus heselhausi* Oudemans, NS99, NT09.

Finally, two specimens were sent to me for confirmation of identity. They are:

Rhadinopsylla pentacantha (Rothschild), 1 from mole nest, nr. Kilbagie, – iii.64, M.B. Usher, NS9391 and *Spilopsyllus cuniculi* (Dale), 1 female from body of *Lepus europaeus*, Aitkenhead Forest Mill, 8.i.64, A.R. Mead-Briggs, NS 940940.

This all adds up to a rather poor list and an immense dearth of collecting and much more must be done before a final list can be published. The following points arise:

a) The scope for more collecting leads the naturalist initially to the common species. For instance no cat fleas have been recorded, they will be found on most cats and dogs and, perhaps, the much less common dog flea. There are two species to be found on shrews, one in sand martin nests, three in house martin nests, two in nesting boxes, up to six in vole nests, one on badgers. Bird nests in damp areas are likely to have up to three species, wheatear nests have another. The nests of Corvidae possibly another couple. Few of our bird fleas and no bat fleas have been recorded from the County.

It must be remembered that bird nests must not be interfered with whilst still in use.

b) Most of the records are old and the species concerned have been recorded from single localities. Re-recording is a necessity.

c) The need for cross-co-operation between naturalists of different disciplines is necessary. The siphonapterist is largely in the hands of mammalogists and ornithologists if his work is to be successful. Members of both groups should become actively interested in the ectoparasites of the vertebrates in which they profess to be involved. Veterinarians and staff at the various kinds of animal refuges could help. Making local lists is an activity in which secondary school pupils can be involved, e.g. my first paper, the first paper on fleas of Gloucestershire, was done with a very considerable amount of assistance of my pupils.

d) The need for authors of papers at all levels to give full data when writing their papers when otherwise much information is lost.

References

Mead-Briggs, A.R. and Page, R.J.C., (1964). Fleas other than *Spilopsyllus cuniculi* Dale from a collection of rabbits predominantly myxomatous, obtained throughout Great Britain. *Entomologists's Gaz.*, 15, 60-65.

Mead-Briggs, A.R. and Page, R.J.C., (1964). Records of rabbit fleas, *Spilopsyllus cuniculi* (Dale), from every county in Great Britain with notes on infestation rates. *Entomologists's Monthly Magazine*, 100: 8-17.

Rothschild, M., (1952). A collection of fleas from the bodies of British birds, with notes on their distribution and host preferences. *Bulletin British Museum (Natural History) Entomology*, 2: 187-232.

Smit, F.G.A.M., (1957). The recorded distribution and hosts of Siphonaptera in Britain. *Entomologist's Gazette*, 8: 45-75.

Thompson, G.B., (1958). The parasites of British Birds and mammals XXXIII. The insect ectoparasites of the House Sparrow (*Passer d.domesticus L.*) *Entomologist's Monthly Magazine* 94: 1-5.

Usher, M.B., (1968). Notes on *Ctenophthalmus nobilis* (Rothschild) Scotland. *Entomologists's Gazette*, 19: 223-228.

Waterston, J., (1909). On some Scottish Siphonaptera II. *Ann. Scot. Natural History*, 72: 226-228.

Hystrichopsylla t. talpae (Curtis).
Britain's largest flea – a flea on moles, voles, field mice and shrews.
(Photo: David de Courscy Henshaw.)

BOOK REVIEWS

There are three recent Stenlake Publishing books of local historic annotated photographs, by author Guthrie Hutton, of c 50pp, and priced £7.50 – **Old Alloa, Old Clackmannan, Old Kinross.**

The White Phantom of the Loch. Maxwell Gordon. EOS Verlag, St. Ottilien. 200pp. ISBN 3 8306 7115 6.
£4.99. (distributor Mrs Barkway, 2a St. Michael Dr. Helensburgh).
Intrigeing ghost stories and reminiscences based on the author's knowledge and experiences of the legendary loch, and focusing on some 18 tragic accidents on and off the water over the years.

Discovery and Excavation in Scotland. Ed. Robin Turner. The Journal of the Council for Scottish *Archaeology*. 2002. 180pp.
Brief reports by local authority areas – includes for Stirling – Dunblane Cathedral, Clachie Burn, East Coldoch, Jail Wynd, Station Square.

Gargunnock, Parish, Village, Guest House. Ian McCallum, author and publisher, Trelawney Cottage, the Square. 136pp. ISBN 0 9541263 0 0. £12.
Includes – 1832 voters, War 1 veterans, ministers, farmers, feuers, 1881 census, has colour illustrations, and plans.

Scottish Pottery Historical Review no. 22, 2002. Scottish Pottery Society. Editor Robert Rankine, Alloa. 72pp.
Includes papers on – 30 years of the Society; New light on Alloa pottery; by Susan Mills – a Bailey Australian export teapot, a dish found at Bauchop's House; also on Dunmore Pottery, and Peter Gardner's Centenary.

An Archaeological Field Survey of Leny Wood at the Pass of Leny. Ed. P. J. Wilson. Association of Certificated Archaeologists (Glasgow University), Occasional paper no. 53. 2002. 70pp. ISBN 9542590 0 9. (not saleable – though donations welcome).
78 features described and illustrated – platforms, stone structures, peat bog, quarry scoop.

Around Doune and Deanston; Images of Scotland. Karen Ross. Tempus Publishing. 128pp. ISBN 0 7524 2768 7. £11.99.
A fine pictorial and factual complement / supplement to the FNH's Doune; historical notes, by Moray Mackay, now being reprinted by the Kilmadock Trust, Doune.

Glasgow's Other River – the Kelvin. Alex Matheson. Port Publishing, Ayr. 260pp. ISBN 0 9516576 2m 0. £12.99.

THE DISTRIBUTION OF LAMPREYS IN THE RIVER TEITH

Peter S. Maitland and Alex A. Lyle

"The fishermen in the Forth, above Alloa, when they accidentally take Lampreys in their nets, invariably return them again to the water having a prejudice against them. Thus they are never under any circumstances seen in the Edinburgh markets." (Parnell, 1838)

SUMMARY

Three lamprey species occur in Scotland – River Lamprey (*Lampetra fluviatilis*), Brook Lamprey (*Lampetra planeri*) and Sea Lamprey (*Petromyzon marinus*). This study describes the distribution of lampreys in the main stem of the River Teith, a major initial objective being to define the upper and lower limits in order to set boundaries for the proposed Special Area of Conservation.

The upper reaches of the River Teith are fast flowing and among the dominant stones and boulders there is little sand to provide habitat for young lampreys. Only below the farms of Inverlochlarig and Blaircreich do suitable silty sand beds start to appear and in them ammocoete larvae, which become common in most suitable places further downstream. Thus the upper limit of ammocoete distribution is just above the junction of the main river with Allt Sgione.

The lower reaches of the River Teith (now technically the River Forth) have an abundance of larval habitat, but below Stirling Auld Brig, in the tidal estuarine reaches, suitable sandy habitat is rare and replaced in most places by very fine soft silts. Some small areas of sandy silt within Stirling town were found to contain ammocoetes, and the rail bridge there seems to represent the lower limit of their distribution.

All the larvae identified so far in the upper reaches were River or Brook Lampreys and their large size here suggests that they are mostly likely to be Brook Lampreys. Sea Lamprey larvae occur upstream at least as far as Callander and thus the adults must be able to negotiate river obstacles below this, notably the weir at Deanston.

INTRODUCTION

The River Teith is known to support all three native species of lamprey: Sea Lamprey (*Petromyzon marinus*), River Lamprey (*Lampetra fluviatilis*) and the Brook Lamprey (*Lampetra planeri*) (Maitland *et al.*, 1983, 1994). Conservation obligations have arisen from the EU 'Habitats Directive' (1992) which lists all three species in Annex II and thus obliges member states to (a) designate sites to form part of the 'Natura 2000' network comprising Special Areas of Conservation (SACs), (b) protect such sites from deterioration or disturbance with a significant effect on the nature conservation interest (and take steps to conserve that interest), and (c) protect the species of Community interest listed in the Annexes to the Directive (Maitland, 1993, 1995). For this reason, the River Teith, along with several other Scottish rivers, has been proposed by Scottish Natural Heritage as a Special Area of Conservation (SAC) for lampreys. Atlantic Salmon (*Salmo salar*) are present as a qualifying feature, but not a primary reason for site selection.

All three of these lamprey species are very alike in many ways – especially in their life histories in fresh water, where they occupy similar (often the same) habitats for most of their lives (Maitland, 1980). Thus, factors that have affected one species are likely to have affected both others. Similarly, conservation requirements to enhance and restore populations are likely to be very similar for all three species, with the proviso that two species (River Lamprey and Sea Lamprey) require a pathway from their adult feeding grounds in the sea to their spawning grounds, whereas the Brook Lamprey is a purely freshwater species, needing access only between larval and spawning habitats. The larvae of River Lamprey and Brook Lamprey are virtually indistinguishable from one another and it may be that this is just one species with two different life forms (Maitland *et al.*, 1994) or 'paired' species which have only recently separated from one another.

Relatively little research has been carried out on lampreys in the Teith/Forth system. Early work on the River Lamprey in the Forth Estuary (Maitland *et al.*, 1983) was followed by preliminary research on all three species in the River Teith itself (Maitland *et al.*, 1994). During this period the River Teith and other rivers (including the River Endrick and the River Spey) were recommended to the Joint Nature Conservation Committee (Maitland, 1993) as being important sites for lampreys in Great Britain. Subsequent to this, preliminary studies of lampreys in the lower Teith were carried out by Gardiner *et al.* (1995). Work on the seasonal dynamics of adult lampreys in the Forth Estuary continued during this period (Maitland, 1998).

The main objective of the present study was to determine the distribution of all three species of lampreys in the main stem of the River Teith and, in particular, the upper and lower limits of this distribution which would define the boundaries of the proposed Special Area of Conservation.

LAMPREY ECOLOGY

Most species of lamprey have a similar life cycle, which involves the migration of adults upstream into rivers to reach the spawning areas – normally stony or gravelly stretches of running water. There they spawn in pairs or groups, laying eggs in crude nests – shallow depressions created by lifting away small stones with their suckers. These stones surround and sometimes cover and protect the eggs, while the nest itself may often be under a large stone, log or clump of vegetation. Frequently, however, the nest is in the open in shallow water and the spawning adults are very vulnerable to predators. After hatching, the young elongate larvae, known as ammocoetes and only a few millimetres in length, swim or are washed downstream by the current to areas of sandy silt in still water where they burrow and spend the next few years in tunnels. They are blind, the sucker is incomplete and the teeth are undeveloped. Ammocoetes feed by creating a current which draws organic particles (coated with bacteria) and minute plants (such as diatoms) into the pharynx. There they become entwined in a slimy mucus string that is swallowed by the larva. After several years, the number varying with species and habitat, the larvae metamorphose into the adult form, with a complete sucker, distinct eyes and a silvery grey skin. Migration then takes place, either downstream to feed on fish in estuaries or the sea (River and Sea Lampreys) or upstream to spawn (Brook Lamprey) without feeding.

Sea and River Lampreys in the River Teith migrate down to the Forth Estuary (Figure 1) after metamorphosis. Sea Lampreys then seem to move out to sea where their feeding habits are little known, though they do feed on Sea Trout (*Salmo trutta*) to some extent (Smith, 1957). Many River Lampreys, however, remain in the estuary where they feed by using their suckers to attach to and suck blood and flesh from Flounder (*Platichthys flesus*), Herring (*Clupea harengus*) and other common fish species there (Maitland *et al.*, 1984). When they reach adult size, after 1-2 years, they accumulate in the upper estuary in the autumn of each year to start their upstream migration into the Forth/Teith system. In most cases, the adults of the three species can be distinguished by size alone – Brook Lampreys are usually some 10-16 cm, River Lampreys 18-36 cm and Sea Lampreys 40-80 cm.

METHODOLOGY

Prior to field sampling, in addition to personal knowledge of the River Teith, some information was available from an earlier River Corridor Survey (Ecosurveys, 1990). The information in this was analysed, but proved to be of limited value because there was little specific identification of silt beds – at most, usually only an indication that such substrates were present (or absent) in each section surveyed. Information on several sections of the river was not included in the report, nor were the Rivers Larig and Forth nor any of the on-line lochs (Doine, Voil and Lubnaig) surveyed.

After permissions were obtained from relevant owners, each stretch of river (or loch shore) to be sampled was surveyed by walking and examination for habitat suitable for lamprey larvae. In several areas (*e.g.* some parts of the shores of Lochs Doine and Voil), no really suitable substratum was found and so the 'most likely' substratum for larvae was selected for sampling.

Sampling was carried out by electric fishing. The equipment used consisted of a pulsed DC back-pack system operating from a 24 v battery supply and offered a variety of output power, pulse frequency and pulse width options. Throughout sampling, these options were set at 300 v, 50 Hz and 50 % respectively. In use, two workers, side by side, sampled over a previously defined area, one sweeping the area with a ring cathode, both collecting any ammocoetes by hand nets as they appeared from the substratum and were temporarily stunned. Larvae were held in plastic bags which were subsequently labelled, chilled and then frozen. Two sweeps were carried out for each sample area.

After sampling, a full pro forma was completed for each site where lampreys were found and photographs taken of the site. A sketch was made of each site, showing its principal features (substratum, vegetation, etc.). In the laboratory, after thawing, larvae were identified as either *Lampetra* or *Petromyzon* and measured individually for length. All larvae were then preserved in 70 % methyl alcohol and stored.

A secondary objective of the study was to examine likely areas of habitat for Sea Lamprey spawning, either to detect lampreys actually spawning or to locate nests after spawning. In addition to observations carried out at all places in reaches where larvae were sampled, several stretches of river which appeared suitable for spawning or where spawning had previously been reported (*e.g.* at Blairdrummond, Deanston, Lanrick and Callander) were specifically examined when conditions were suitable (*i.e.* low water and adequate sunlight for good visibility). During sampling, anglers and local people were asked if they had ever seen lampreys in the Teith system and information on several locations for spawning sites of all three lamprey species was recorded in this way.

LAMPREY DISTRIBUTION

General

Full details of the distribution of lampreys and related data are available in the final report of the study to Scottish Natural Heritage. For each site where lampreys were recorded this included: numbers of River/Brook and Sea Lampreys and their length-frequencies; a completed site data sheet and sketch; site photographs.

Upper limit

Sampling was started in the River Larig (Figure 1) just below its junction with the Ishag Burn (NGR: 27 416 174). It is believed that there is virtually no suitable larval habitat above this point, the river being fast flowing and rocky along all its course here. The river was examined in detail from the Ishag Burn junction downstream to near Inverlochlarig Farm and all possible larval habitat, however small in extent was noted and electrofished. It was not until Site 7, just below the junction of the Allt Sgione with the River Larig, that the first ammocoete (just one specimen) was found. Below this, exactly at the junction of the Inverlochlarig Burn with the River Larig (Site 8: Inverlochlarig), a silt bed produced several larvae, whilst further downstream large silt beds at Sites 9 (Track Upper) and 10 (Track Lower) were clearly suitable larval habitat and samples of larvae were obtained.

Thus, the realistic upper limit for lamprey larvae in the River Teith is that stretch of the river between the farms of Inverlochlarig and Blaircreich (NGR: 27 438 180). Only here do suitable silty sand beds start to appear and in them ammocoetes (all identified as River/Brook Lamprey). Downstream from this point to the tidal reaches, lamprey larvae were found in almost all suitable substrates examined (Table 1).

Lower limit

At the lower end of the system, now the River Forth, the river was examined in some detail from Stirling Auld Brig downstream as far as Haugh of West Grange. As in the upper reaches, suitable larval habitat was scarce and found only in a few places in the active river channel at low tide. Steep soft banks of fine tidal silts made access difficult. No larvae were found in apparently suitable silts at Site 36 (Cambuskenneth Abbey), where the invertebrate fauna was dominated by brackish water invertebrates (*e.g. Corophium*). One small ammocoete only was found in fine silts at Site 35, just above Cambuskenneth footbridge. Only at Site 34, just below Stirling Auld Brig, were significant numbers of larvae found (Table 1) and both River/Brook larvae and transformers and Sea Lamprey larvae were identified in the sample from here.

Thus, the realistic lower limit for lamprey larvae is that stretch of the river crossed by the three main bridges in Stirling. One apparently suitable silt bed was observed just below the north stanchion of the rail bridge but could not be sampled because of intervening deep water. Thus this bridge could perhaps be regarded as a suitable landmark for the lower limit of larval habitat in the Teith/Forth system (NGR: 26 798 943).

LAMPREY SPECIES

River and Brook Lampreys

River/Brook Lampreys made up by far the greatest number of ammocoetes identified and at all sites where lampreys were found were the dominant species. Because it is not possible to separate most ammocoetes as either River Lamprey or Brook Lamprey, the individual distribution of each of the two species cannot be defined. However, it seems likely that Brook Lamprey is the dominant species in most parts of the Teith system and probably the only one found above the Falls of Leny, which appear to be a significant barrier to the migratory species. Certainly all records of adult lampreys seen spawning at various places in this part of the catchment have been of Brook Lamprey.

Sea Lamprey

As in many other Scottish rivers (Maitland *et al.*, 1994) Sea Lampreys seem to be relatively rare in the Teith system. Even where they occurred in samples collected during the present study, the numbers were very small compared to those of River/Brook Lampreys. This agrees with what is known about Sea and River Lampreys in the estuary where the former is rare but the latter is common (Maitland, 1998) and also with spawning lampreys in the whole of the Teith /Forth system.

This survey has determined that Sea Lampreys do extend upstream as far as Callander but there is no evidence of this species above there and it may well be restricted from further upstream migration by the Falls of Leny. However, it is clear that the large weir at Deanston is not always an obstacle and that Sea Lampreys do occur throughout the main stem of the river, albeit in small numbers. Larvae were recorded at Sites 27 (Callander), 30 (Lanrick Lower), 32 (Mill of Torr) and 34 (Auld Brig).

DENSITIES

General

The numbers of ammocoetes showed great variation from site to site and even within sites. There are probably several reasons for this variation, but much of it is probably determined by habitat quality. Apart from the individual problems of sampling at several sites (see below), some of the sites sampled were clearly of poor quality in relation to what is known about the requirements of ammocoete larvae. These sites were sampled on the basis of being the 'best available' in the stretch of river or shoreline concerned, and it was not surprising that no larvae were found in them. Sites in this category include all of those above Site 7 (Blaircreich Lower), as well as Sites 13 (Doine), 14 (Quarry) in Loch Doine, Site 21 (Tigh na Voil) in Loch Voil and Site 28 (Gart Wood). The implication is that there are no, or very few, larvae in these stretches because of lack of habitat.

The converse is that larvae can be expected to occur anywhere in the main stem of the Teith/Forth system, between Inverlochlarig and Stirling, where suitable habitat is found. Suitable habitat may be defined as soft sandy silts where the current is slow or absent (frequently a slight backwater) and the substrate surface has fine deposits of detritus or algae. Shading by trees or overhanging vegetation appears to make the site more favourable for larvae.

River and Brook Lampreys

The numbers of ammocoete larvae of River/Brook Lampreys ranged from zero at several sites (see above) to over 46 per m^2 at Site 31 (Lanrick Upper). Habitat quality is undoubtedly a major factor, for example at Site 32 (Lanrick Lower), few larvae occurred, even though superficially the site seemed very suitable. However, during sampling it became clear that the site was anoxic below the surface because of numerous dead leaves trapped in the substrate and bubbles of gas were released when it was disturbed. Similarly, high densities at Site 27 (Callander) were not repeated downstream at Site 28 (Gart Wood) where no larvae were found. The latter site, though the 'best available' in the stretch concerned, was poor ammocoete habitat with sparse firm sand among stones. Further upstream, the high densities at Site 22 (Rusgathan) were not repeated at Site 23 (Strathyre) despite the substrate here seeming suitable for ammocoetes. However, this site is the regular landing and launching spot for local canoes and was subject to frequent disturbance.

Sea Lamprey

Even at sites where they occurred, the densities of Sea Lamprey were always low, never reaching as much as one larva per square metre. At such low densities, the probability of catching them is also relatively low and so this species may well be present at sites between Callander and Stirling where it was not actually recorded (*e.g.* Sites 29, 32 and 35). The low densities of this species agree with the findings of other studies, both in the Teith itself (Gardiner *et al.*, 1995) and in other rivers, for example the River Leven (Maitland *et al.*, 1994).

SIZE

River and Brook Lampreys

The largest River/Brook Lamprey larva recorded was found at Site 7 (Blaircreich Lower) and was the only specimen recorded over 140 mm – all other larvae were less than 130 mm. This is substantially less than those found in the neighbouring Lomond catchment, where larvae of Brook Lampreys over 130 mm are common (Maitland *et al.*, 1994).

Small larvae (less than 25 mm) were also uncommon. This may mean that few 0+ animals were present in the areas fished or that they were too small to be detected. Also, as the time of sampling (July) is not long after the normal spawning period of River/Brook Lampreys, many larvae may not have fully dispersed from the spawning grounds.

Although most of the larger larvae (*i.e.* >110 mm) collected during the survey were found above the Falls of Leny, the greatest proportion of the smaller larvae (<40 mm) were found here. This could be related to the fact that one of the main differences between these two populations of ammocoetes is that those animals above the falls may all be Brook Lampreys, whereas those below are like to be a mixture of River and Brook Lampreys.

Where larvae were numerous enough for the length-frequencies to be meaningful, the distributions of the size groups varied among the different sites. For example at Site 9 (Track Upper) a wide range of sizes was found, whereas at Site 10 (Track Lower) most larvae were from 31-43 mm in length. Small larvae also dominated at Sites 25 (Cui Beithe), 33 (Doune Castle) and 34 (Mill of Torr) whereas at Sites 16 (Monachyle) 29 (Torrie) and 36 (Auld Brig) larger larvae dominated. It is likely that these differences reflect the varying success of recruitment of young from local spawning areas to different sites in different years

Sea Lamprey

The numbers of Sea Lamprey larvae were so low that it is impossible to come to any meaningful conclusions regarding sizes, which ranged from 25-92 mm.

SPAWNING SITES

River and Brook Lampreys

All the River/Brook Lamprey spawning sites which have been reported in the Teith system appear to be of Brook Lampreys (Table 2). The only definite sites for River Lampreys are in the Forth catchment – in the River Devon near Tillicoultry and the Mye Burn near Buchlyvie. However, as the spawning requirements of the two species are very similar (Huggins and Thompson, 1970) it seems certain that River Lampreys do spawn in the main stem of the River Teith, though whether they are able to negotiate the weir at Deanston is uncertain.

Sea Lamprey

Though no new spawning sites for Sea Lampreys were located during this study, several have been recorded in past years, mostly in the middle sections of the river between Deanston and the junction with the River Forth.

DISCUSSION

Methodology

At the beginning of this study it was hoped that a previous River Corridor Survey of the Teith would be helpful in identifying the main areas of substrate suitable for ammocoete larvae. This proved not to be the case, however, as riverine substrates are not clearly identified using standard River Corridor methodology. This is something which could be rectified in the future, however, for at low to moderate water levels ammocoete beds are readily recognisable and could be mapped.

There remain problems with the sampling methodology largely because of the varying size and nature of the habitats which ammocoetes inhabit and their variable dispersal within these habitats. Strategies for future sampling must consider the objectives in relation to the effort available and it may be that relative, semi-quantitative methods such as time sampling may be more useful than time-consuming mark-recapture methods or attempts at fully quantitative sampling, which, by definition, require several accurate samples at each site.

The area of substratum sampled varied greatly from site to site. In the upper reaches of the River Teith only small patches of sands and gravels were present (often less than one square metre) but these were electrofished in the standard way as the only potential ammocoete habitat available. Further downstream, where greater stretches of habitat were found, larger areas were sampled (rather than a standard one square metre) because, due to the patchy nature of ammocoete distribution within some silt beds, small samples might well contain no lampreys even though they were present elsewhere in the same silt bed. At several sites for example, although more than 5 m² were sampled, only one ammocoete was found. Using smaller sampling areas, such sites would probably be regarded as negative for ammocoetes. Site 18 (Muirlaggan East, with only one ammocoete found in 25 m²) is an extreme example of this.

During the present study it was very clear that sampling efficiency varied from site to site. Problems encountered which lowered accuracy include (a) ammocoetes escaping at the fringes of the area shocked, especially where numbers were high and several animals had to be netted at once (*e.g.* Site 43:

Mill of Torr), (b) poor visibility during fishing due to cloud cover, overhanging trees or fine silt disturbed during netting (*e.g.* Site 17: Muirlaggan West), (c) difficulty in actually netting shocked larvae because of sunken branches or stones, etc. projecting from the substrate (*e.g.* Site 31: Lanrick Upper), (d) problems of physical access to silt beds because of steep muddy banks (*e.g.* Site 37: Cambuskenneth), very soft silts (*e.g.* Site 32: Lanrick Lower), or steeply shelving shore into deep water (*e.g.* Site 18: House Burn Delta).

Future research

Apart from further studies of methodology there are clearly a number of lines of research worthy of pursuit in relation to lamprey conservation in the Teith and other rivers. One of these relates to the difficulty of separating the larvae of River and Brook Lampreys and thus their distribution in rivers. One approach to this problem is to give consideration to a project where batches of older larvae from specified sites in the river were reared to transformation (Maitland *et al.*, 1983) and thus could be identified (Hardisty, 1970, Bird and Potter, 1979). Larvae are relatively easy to keep and rear in captivity and batches from individual sites could be kept until metamorphosis in individual site tanks or, after tagging, in communal tanks.

Another area of future research, which is relevant to lampreys in a number of Scottish catchments, is the relative importance of lake sediments as nursery grounds for ammocoete larvae. Larvae were found in appropriate sediments in the Teith lochs and were abundant in some places (*e.g.* Site 16: Monachyle). They are also known to occur in sediments in lochs in other parts of Scotland (*e.g.* Loch Lomond, Loch Ness) and it seems likely that these lacustrine sediments are an important habitat for Brook Lampreys in many areas.

Conservation

The primary reason for the selection of the River Teith as an SAC is that this river supports high densities of River and Brook Lampreys and also a population of Sea Lampreys. The conservation importance of the River Teith is increased by the fact that, unlike many other British rivers, it supports populations of all three lamprey species. The river provides excellent habitat with usually pristine water quality, well-vegetated banks and a substantially unaltered river channel. Below Deanston there are no significant barriers to migration and the necessary habitat types to support the full life cycle of lampreys are present in many places. Atlantic Salmon are present as a qualifying feature. The fact that much of the River Teith SAC lies within the Loch Lomond and the Trossachs National Park should aid conservation of the river and clearly adds to the scientific importance of the fish communities within the Park (Maitland, 2002).

Conservation of lampreys in the River Teith requires initial debate followed by the development of management philosophies and practices (Maitland, 1997, 1998). Problems related to the difficulty of ammocoete identification, the shortage of suitable larval habitat in some parts of the upper and middle reaches (where, in some places, this may be due to human impact) and the apparent scarcity of Sea Lampreys within the river system as a whole are aspects worthy of consideration. Reasons for the low numbers of Sea Lampreys require further investigation since this species is much more fecund than either River of Brook Lampreys (Hardisty, 1964) and larger numbers of larvae would have been expected at least in some parts of the lower river. The fact that River Lampreys and Sea Lampreys are both very important commercial species in some parts of Europe means that the case for their conservation rests on potential economic as well as biodiversity concepts.

Pressures on the lamprey stocks in the River Teith can include various types of river engineering (especially where these affect silt beds), removal of gravels and sand, pollution from sewage works, septic tanks and agriculture, predation during spawning from predators (*e.g.* Herons, Goosanders, etc.) and disturbance by anglers and recreational users. It seems too that there is antagonism to lampreys from some anglers – the severed head of a large Sea Lamprey was found some years ago just below the Teith/Forth junction and anglers have been known to kill spawning Sea Lampreys in the neighbouring Lomond catchment. Education to reduce prejudice within the angling community may well be beneficial to lampreys in the future.

During this study it was apparent that, in some silt beds, ammocoetes were far more numerous in some parts than in others. Research to understand the reasons for such variation would help, not only with the management of larval habitat throughout the river, but also with sampling methodologies for any future monitoring. Such a study might also give a better understanding of the requirements of Sea Lamprey larvae which may favour some sections of river or types of substratum over others.

Spawning sites for Sea Lampreys

The fact that there appears to be an abundance of spawning habitat for Sea Lampreys, but a relatively small population, has made it difficult to detect any spawning activity or nests during this study. However, the fact that anglers are regularly on the river at spawning time and that some have reported seeing spawning lampreys would indicate that anglers could make a valuable contribution to our knowledge of spawning grounds by reporting any observations of spawning animals to the local fisheries officer.

ACKNOWLEDGEMENTS

This project was funded by Scottish Natural Heritage. We are grateful to SNH staff, particularly Ross Johnston and Jim McIntosh for their help and advice during this project. Owners of most parts of the river were very co-operative in allowing us to sample and we would like to thank in particular: Mr P. Brown, Mr G.T. Cumming, Mr D.A.J. Dickson, Mr and Mrs B.G. Hughes, Mr Robert Lewis, Mr Malcolm McNaughton and family, Mr Richard Muir, Mrs Oldham, Cambusmore Estate Trust, Cowanes Trust, Forest Enterprise (Mr Mike Stewart), Moray Estate (Mr Connell) and Stirling Council. Particular thanks are due to Alex Kirika for his help with sampling in the field, and to the Forth

Fishery Foundation (Mr A. Fell and Mr D.A.J. Dickson) and the Forth District Salmon Fishery Board (Mr T. Mackenzie) for information and advice.

REFERENCES

Bird, D.J. and Potter, I.C. (1979). Metamorphosis in the paired species of lampreys, *Lampetra fluviatilis* (L.) and *Lampetra planeri* (Bloch). 2. Quantitative data for body proportions, weights, lengths and sex ratios. *Journal of the Linnaean Society of London* 65, 127-143.

Ecosurveys Ltd. (1990). *1990 River Corridor Survey. River Teith and Tributaries (R. Balvag, Garbh Uisge and Braceland Burn).* Ecosurveys Ltd.

Gardiner, R., Taylor, R. and Armstrong, J. (1995). Habitat assessment and survey of lamprey populations occurring in areas of conservation interest. *Fisheries Research Services Report* 4/95, 1-18.

Hardisty, M.W. (1964). The fecundity of lampreys. *Archiv fur Hydrobiologie* 60, 340-357.

Hardisty, M.W. (1970). The relationship of gonadal development to the life cycles of the paired species of lamprey, *Lampetra fluviatilis* (L.) and *Lampetra planeri* (Bloch). *Journal of Fish Biology* 2, 173-181.

Huggins, R.J. and Thompson, A. (1970). Communal spawning of Brook and River Lampreys, *Lampetra planeri* Bloch and *Lampetra fluviatilis* L. *Journal of Fish Biology* 2, 53-54.

Maitland, P.S. (1980). Review of the ecology of lampreys in northern Europe. *Canadian Journal of Fisheries and Aquatic Sciences* 37, 1944-1952.

Maitland, P.S. (1993). *Sites in Great Britain for freshwater and estuarine fish on the EC Habitats and Species Directive.* Report to JNCC, Peterborough.

Maitland, P.S. (1995). *Freshwater fish of Annexes II and IV of the EC Habitats Directive (92/43/EEC).* Report to the European Commission, Brussels.

Maitland, P.S. (1997). *Species Action Plans for lampreys in England.* Report to English Nature, Peterborough.

Maitland, P.S. (1998). Fish entrainment at power stations on the Firth of Forth. Report to Scottish power, Kincardine on Forth.

Maitland, P.S. (2002). Freshwater fish of the Loch Lomond and the Trossachs National Park. *Forth Naturalist and Historian* 25, 53-64.

Maitland, P.S., East, K. and Morris, K.H. (1983). Lamprey populations in the catchments of the Forth and Clyde estuaries. *Annual Report of the Institute of Terrestrial Ecology* 1983, 17-18.

Maitland, P.S., Morris, K.H. and East, K. (1994). The ecology of lampreys (Petromyzonidae) in the Loch Lomond area. *Hydrobiologia* 290, 105-120.

Maitland, P.S., Morris, K.H., East, K., Schoonoord, M.P., Van der Wal, B. and Potter, I.C. (1984). The estuarine biology of the River Lamprey, *Lampetra fluviatilis*, in the Firth of Forth, Scotland, with particular reference to size composition and feeding. *Journal of Zoology, London.* 203, 211-225.

Parnell, R. (1838). *The Natural History of the Fishes of the Firth of Forth.* Memoirs of the Wernarian Natural History Society, Edinburgh.

Smith, I.W. (1957). The occurrence of damaged sea trout on the east coast of Scotland. *Salmon and Trout Magazine* 1957, 148-150.

Table 1. Number of lampreys per 10m^2 at sites on the main stem of the River Teith (see Figure 1).

RIVER OR LOCH	SITE	BANK	NGR	Brook/River Lamprey	Sea Lamprey
LARIG	1. Junction	L	27 4165 1746	0	0
		R	27 4164 1742	0	0
	2. Braes	L	27 4213 1749	0	0
		R	27 4213 1748	0	0
	3. Drumlich	L	27 4222 1738	0	0
		R	27 4233 1737	0	0
	4. Mhicgriogair	L	27 4269 1744	0	0
		L	27 4275 1749	0	0
	5. Ford	L	27 4315 1778	0	0
	6. Blaircreich Upper	L	27 4367 1803	0	0
		R	27 4368 1802	0	0
	7. Blaircreich Lower	R	27 4388 1807	1	0
	8. Inverlochlarig	L	27 4447 1828	12	0
	9. Track Upper	R	27 4469 1826	21	0
	10. Track Lower	L	27 4490 1827	82	0
DOINE	11. Carnaig	L	27 4630 1896	23	0
	12. Creagan Loisgte	L	27 4618 1913	2	0
	13. Doine 153m	L	27 4672 1933	0	0
	14. Quarry	L	27 4711 1938	0	0
	15. Monachylemhor	L	27 4748 1945	0	0
VOIL	16. Monachyle	L	27 4784 1938	25	0
	17. Muirlaggan West	R	27 5118 2000	30	0
	18. House Burn Delta	R	27 5145 2005	11	0
	19. Muirlaggan East	R	27 5154 2009	1	0
	20. Stronvar	R	27 5323 2073	9	0
	21. Tigh na Voil	L	27 5311 2052	0	0
BALVAG	22. Rusgachan	L	27 5620 1872	350	0
	23. Strathyre	L	27 5595 1682	11	0
LUBNAIG	24. Laggan	R	27 5646 1457	10	0
	25. Cuil Beithe	L	27 5802 1376	210	0
	26. Crannog	R	27 5835 1092	1	0
TEITH	27. Callander	L	27 6238 0772	207	9
	28. Gart Wood	L	27 6400 0550	0	0
	29. Torrie	R	27 6701 0483	163	0
	30. Tynasprit	L	27 6608 0457	27	0
	31. Lanrick Upper	R	27 6713 0345	465	4
	32. Lanrick Lower	L	27 7000 0286	40	1
		R	27 7016 0273	41	0
	33. Doune Castle	L	26 7286 0086	47	1
	34. Mill of Torr	L	26 7442 9904	185	3
FORTH	35. Kildean	R	26 7855 9542	32	0
	36. Auld Brig	R	26 7968 9454	40	1
	37. Cambuskenneth	R	26 8051 9407	1	0
	38. C'kenneth Abbey	L	26 8100 9372	0	0

Table 2. Records of lampreys, mostly spawning, from different parts of the Forth/Teith catchment.

BROOK LAMPREY

Monachyle Burn, lower part above loch (1992, 1999: Forth District Salmon Fishery Board)
Inverlochlarig Burn, next to farm (1996: FDSFB)
River Larig, near junction with Inverlochlarig Burn (1999: F. MacNaughton)
Burn west of Tom na Cloiche (Loch Doine) (2000: local caravan owner)
Muirlaggan House Burn (Loch Doine) (2000: Mr Oldham)
Invernenty Burn, south side of Loch Doine (1996: FDSFB)
Kirkton Burn at Balquhidder (1996: FDSFB)
River Balvag at bridge just south of Balqhidder (1996: FDSFB)
Exchange Burn, in Strathyre (1996: FDSFB)
River Balvag, just east of Strathyre (2000, Mr Gothard)
Middle burn of three east of Tom Bheithe (Loch Lubnaig) (2000: Mr Gothard)
Trean Burn, at Kilmahog (1996: FDSFB)
Foot of Milton Burn above Loch Venachar (1996: FDSFB)
Blackwater near Finlas junction, Brig O' Turk (1996: FDSFB)
Allt Carraig, near Doune (1992: FDSFB)
Mill Lade at Deanston, dozens killed by concreting (1992: FDSFB)
River Devon, just above Tillicoultry (1986: P.S. Maitland) – seen and spawning

RIVER LAMPREY

River Teith at Deanston (1981: P.S. Maitland) - ripe adults trapped
Mye Burn (Forth), near Buchlyvie (1981: FRPB, P.S. Maitland) – seen spawning
River Devon (Forth), just above Tillicoultry (1991: P.S. Maitland) – seen and photographed spawning

SEA LAMPREY

River Teith, Red Brae Pool on Blairdrummond stretch above Ochtertyre (2000: FDSFB)
River Teith, Deanston, near junction with Annet Burn (1981: P.S. Maitland)
River Teith, Deanston, below main weir (Mr Baird)
River Teith, Deanston, at main weir (Mr Thomson)
River Teith, below Doune Castle (man interviewed at Deanston distillery)
River Teith near Cambusmore (Mr T. Mackenzie)
River Teith (Forth), near Old Mills Farm (Mr T. Mackenzie)
River Teith (Forth), above junction with Allan Water (1991: P.S. Maitland) – dead specimen

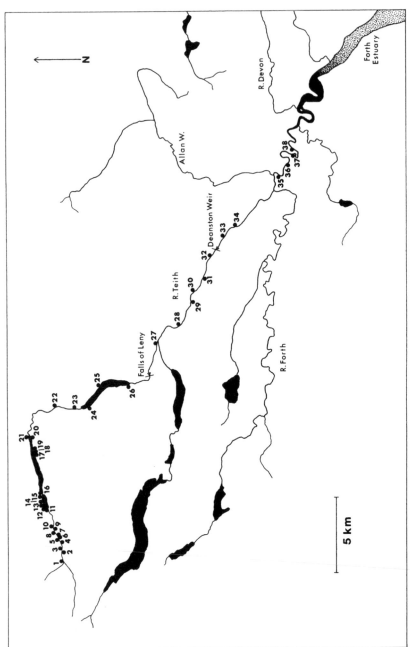

Figure 1. The River Teith (and associated waters) with the location of the 38 sites sampled there for lamprey larvae during 2000.

WEATHER RECORDS FOR CENTRAL SCOTLAND 1651-1659: THE DIARIES OF JOHN LAMONT AND JOHN NICHOLL

Alastair G. Dawson

Introduction

The study of historical climatology in Scotland is in its infancy. Libraries abound with records of past weather but very rarely have these been investigated. Often, these accounts hidden away in dusty shelves provide fascinating insights into the weather experienced by our ancestors. In our modern world we often consider the context of our present climate within the notion of "global warming". We often read that the climate and weather that we experience is extremely benign compared to the harsh conditions that our predecessors experience during the so-called "Little Ice Age" that took place during the 14th- 19th centuries. Yet we know very little about the day to day weather of the "Little Ice Age". For Scotland, much of this information remains unexplored and hidden away in diaries and letters in various archives scattered around the country.

Two men who kept such diaries during the 17th century are John Lamont and John Nicholl. John Lamont was a farmer at Newton in Kennoway Parish in Fife. He kept a diary for the period 1649-1671 within which descriptions of past weather are scattered around accounts of his personal life. Similarly John Nicholl, also from Fife, kept a diary for the period 1650-1667. These two diaries cover some momentous times in Scotland's political history yet within them are unique and precious records of past weather. In the following sections, transcriptions of these accounts are given for the decade 1651-1659. They provide vivid accounts of weather conditions during a decade within the "Little Ice Age". They show very clearly, for example in their descriptions of a drought year, that severe cold was not a characteristic feature and, in so doing, provide a poignant reminder that climate change is an extremely complex process. I quote the accounts verbatim for purposes of precision and accuracy and also to enable the reader to step briefly into the lives of two extraordinary people. Only the words in italics have been added to their accounts

1651 This year a severe famine is reported in Nicoll's Diary (pp. 74-75) "...Much pepill killed this yeir in Scotland, and the riches of this natioun robbed and spoyled out of the toun of Dundie, eftir the storming, quahairin the famin wer hid for saiftie. Great dearth this yeir, the boll of beir being at twentie pund Scottis the boll in mony pairtes of the cuntrey".

1652 This year was characterised by an extremely severe summer drought and a plentiful harvest. Lamont records (pp.45-50) "...All this summer ther was ane extraordinary great drought throwout the wholle kingdome, with great heate, fewe rains; the corns generallie both short and thin, the best grounds worst cornes. (Ther be none liueing that remembers a dryer summer); the grasse brunt vp, the blowms of the pease wallowed (withered) a fourtnight before

Lammis, wheras some years they continowe till Michelmisse. In November. and December "…The wheat, after it was sowen, did spring againe in seuerall places in the shyre of Fyfe, betuixt 9 and 12 dayes; about this tyme also, the greatest pairt of all the tries, whither fruit tries of other tries, begane to bud againe. The whine generallie did blome, and some brome also, in some places. The veilet also had its floure, (which is not ordinar till March); the fege trie young feggs; the crawes also, in some places, begane to gather sticks to ther old nests; strawberries leaues blomed the first of Jan. 1653.

Nicoll (pp. 98-103) states that, "… In Julij, 1652, the cornes being neir rype, much thame wer schorne; and, in the beginning of August, het harvest; the soomer this yeir being exceiding het and fair, the lyke quhairof wes nevir sene in this cuntrey, for the quhilk thair wes much scheiring in Julij the same yeir. This yeir, Michaelmes moone, 1652, wes not sene the space of nyne dayis or thairby, albeit the sky all that tyme wes very cleir, and the weather very fair. This wes for nyne dayis eftir the change. I can not omitt the remembrance of this rair and singular yeir 1652, quihilk not onlie producit ane airlie harvest, sum cornes being ryped and schorne in Junij, (yit not much,) yit in mony pairtes in Julij, and all in August, without weit, storme, and tempest; bot also yeir producit rype wyneberries and graps, and abundance of Scottis chestanes oppinlie fauld at the mercat croce of Edinburgh, and bakin in paistes at bankettis.

This yeir, be ressoun of the continuall heattis all the monethis till the end of December, and eftir that to the 3 of Januar 1653, and of the extraordiner fair weather during that tyme, was the occasioun that the fruit treyis to bud and floorische, and sum of thame to bring furth fruitt, albeit not in perfectioun; foulles began to big thair nestis, and lay eggis evin at or neir Martymes; swa that this yeir in effect producit twa someris. 21 of November 1652. Thair fell out great thunder and fyre at and about four in the morning, being Sonday, quhilk brak doun a freat pairt of the steipill of Dyfert, and rent asunder the stanes thairof. Much micht be spokin of the heat and fair weather of this yeir 1652, quhich producit mony rarities as is befoir mentionat. Amongis utheris, I can not forget to set doun heir that, upone the 27 of November this yeir, sellettis and sybees wer oppinlie cryed and sauld in Edinburgh; and ficklyke fresche hering, indured, and wer oppinlie sauld in November 1652, December, and a great pairt of Januar thaireftir, in anno 1653, abundantlie plentifull and chaip.

1653 Lamont (pp.63) describes the summer of 1653 as "….generally through all Scotland, the corns were att a great rate: beare, oatts, and pease being 11, 12, 13 lib. the bolle; wheate 14 and 15 lib. the bolle; bot after the crope was brought in to the corne yeards, (this crope being more plentifull and large, both in corne and stra, blissed be God, then hath beine for seuerall yeares preceiding), the prices fell strangelie, to the admiration of many, so that from Michelmis 1653 till the end of the yeare, beare, oatts, and pease, was at 4 lib. and 4 lib. 10s. att most; wheat 7 and 8 the bolle; cheese, this summer at 30s. the stone, and the best at 40s. the stone, wooll at 7 and 8 lib. the stone, and the darrest at 12 lib. and 20 marke the stone. Things continued at the cheapnesse, or rather cheaper, oatts beign at 5 marke the bolle, and 12 bolls for 10; till Mairtimis 1655.

Nicoll (pp. 112-120) reports that at the end of August "....and many dayis of September 1653, thair wer great windis, stormes, and tempestis, almoist throw all Ewrop, both be sea and land, be ressoun quhairof mony schips, barkes, and veschellis did perische. This yeir 1653 haid plenty of cornes and very chaip. The meall of the best foirt at 4 lib the boll. The quheit, beir, peas, and beanis proportionallie. The harvest and winter very dry, so that fra October 1653, till the 15 of Marche thaireftir, in anno 1654, thair wes not full sevin schouris, as salbe declairit in the awin place: besyde, this harvest and winter wes exceiding hett; sa that in effect thair wes no winter, the season being both warme and dry.

1654 We turn to Lamont (pp.76-81) for descriptions of the weather of 1654, "…Ther was mutch old corne standing in many of the barne yeards of Fyfe, the like of which was not feine for the space of many yeares before, viz. at Lundie, 7 large oatte stackes, 1 pease stacke, besyde seuerall oatte stackes; at Gilston, (for it was set this 1654 yeare to one Jhone Mairtin, wha laboured before, Blebo in Fyfe); at Largo, seuerall stackes; at Athernie, 4 or 5; at Sconie some; at Drameldrie, in Dauid Auchmuties, some; also att Balgromo, and diuers other places. Also, Agust 1, 1655, ther was some old oatte stackes standing in the barne yearde of Lundy, viz. of the crope 1653. In November ther was seuerall great wynds, so that vp and doune the Firth ther perished severall small vessells; in some the men were safe, in others the men were lost. It blewe doune also some great tries, viz. in Lundie and Largo. 24 Nou. Ther perished a ship neare Inchcome, leaden with iron and lint; the men were safe, and some of the goods. This month ther was a party of Middeltons forces taken by the English vpon the braes of Angus, they being pursewed thrie days, the snow being thicke; namlie, the Lord Kinnoule, Lord Didope, Charles Arskine, Kellies brother, Lo. Coll. Mercer, and 16 more officers, with 62 souldiers.

John Nicoll (pp. 122-139) adds that, "…This last winter, in anno 1653, and all Januar, Februar, and till the 21 of Marche 1654, wes exceiding dry and fair wethir, sa that fra October 1653, till the 21 of Marche thaireftir, in anno 1654, thair wer not above fex schoures of weit or snow, and twa of these schoures fell out on twa severall Sondayis, sua that in effect thair were twa someris. On the 13 Junij 1654 greyne peyis oppinlie sauld in Edinburgh full and ryp. Lykewyse chereyis rype and great sauld at the same tyme, and sum dayis of befoir. On the 24 Julij, cornes wer schorne about Edinburgh; not much this day, bot it fell out that in the end of that moneth, and in the begynning of August, thair wes much scheiring. This former 1654 producit much abundance of cornes, and much abundance of fruitt, in all the corneris of the land, and exceiding chaip, as the lyke was nevir sene in this natioun.

All this somer and harvest, anno 1654, thair fell out ane exceiding great drouth throw all the pairtes of Lothiane, and from Berwik to Glasgow, bot speciallie about Edinburgh, quhairin all the wellis wer dryed up, sa that the inhabitantes could not get sufficient for ordoring thair meatt, and watter could be fund. Notwithstanding all the west cuntrey, from Glasgow to the Rynes of Galloway, haid moir nor ordiner abundance of rayne and weitt. During October 1654, "… All this tyme, and sensyne, thair continued great drouth in all the wellis in Edinburgh, and throgh all the land of Lothiane, so that the pepill in Edinburgh wer constrayned to go abroad the space of ane myle, befoir thai could get ony cleane watter, ather for brewing of aill or beir, or for thair pott meitt. Later, in November 1654 (p.143) ... thair wes great stormes both by sea and land, quhairin sindry schipes and barkis, cuming and going to and fra France, Spayne, England, Yreland, Flanderis, Swaydin, and uther pairtes in Europ, wer caft away and perisched; much skaith also done be land both to man and beast.

1655 Lamont" (pp.91-95) reports that during August, "....All this monthe for the most pairt were many great rayns: Bot about the end of the month they encreased greatlie, so that the bourns ran downe some shorne cornes in severall places; also the bowes of some bridges in Louthian, as also a pairt of some mylls ther; and att St Androus, a pairt of a mille that belongs to Nyddie, called Gappies Mille, as also the Bow Bridge att the shoares of St Androus; and att Lundie Mille, the water entred the mille doore, beate stronglie vpon the walls of the houses ther, ran ouer the head of the bridge, it being higher, by a foote or halfe a foote, then the bridge it selfe; ran away some of the strapping stone att Nether Largo, which had beine unremoved for the space of many yeares before. All this was done by the violence and speate of the rayne water. *During October,* "....there were many great and excessive rayns, so that togither ther was not two dayes wherin ther was not some rayne, by reason of which several houses of the meaner sort of peopell did fall downe to the grounde. He describes how on December 10th, "... being Moneday - all that day, for the most pairt, it did snow, bot at night ther fell extraordinar mutch snow, and all that night ther blew a great wynde, which occasioned great losse and damage to the shyre of Fyfe, both by sea and land. As for the sea, it did flow far aboue its [ordinar] limits and bankes, so that if it had beine...to be a deipe neipe tyde...(as some thinke, it wold exceided Cori [vreckan]...were many small barkes and other vessels that perished, even laying in harbrees, as in Enster, Dysert 20, Craill 30. Also piers were doung downein severall places, as in St Androus, Enster, Craill, Weymes, Leith; a pairt of the Salt girnell in Leuen broken downe; many sheipe, in seuerall places, ouerblowen by the snow and perished; some lesser houses blowen downe; severall tries, in severall places, blowen ouer and broken by the violence of this storme; also several salt panns wronged, both in Fyfe and Louthian syde.

Nicoll (pp. 149-156) describes February 1655 as, "...wes exceiding foull and filthie wether, so that nather plewing, harrowing, nor sawing could be haid for the great and frequency raynes that fell out. It is thocht, that this moneth of Februar and a pairt of Marche following producity moir weit and foull weather nor the twa yeiris preceiding, viz. The yeris of our Lord 1653 and 1654, these two yeris being exceiding het and dry yeiris, and abundantlie fruitfull. Farder, it wald be remembered, that at this tyme, viz. Both befoir Lambes and thaireftir, in this anno 1655, thair fell out extraordiner schoures of weit and rayne, quhairof the lyke wes seldome sene, continuing mony nyghtes and dayis togidder without intermissioun, to the great destruction of that crop and cornes than growand, batterand the famin to the ground, and destroyand alluterlie all the crop of peyis. This unseasonable seasone pat mony in fear of dearth and famyne, and justlie; because plentie of victuell wes comptit a plaig to many, quha haiffing great stoir of victuell, could not haiff such pryces thairfoir as in the lait yeiris preceding. For these thrie yeiris bypast, the victuell of all foirtes wes exceiding chaipe by expectatioun, viz the best peck of meill in the mercat of Edinburgh being sauld and bocht for ane groat, and sumtyme for thrie schilling and ane plak; and being bocht in bollis wes sumtyme sauld for fyftir schilling, and sum uther tymes for xlviijs; the boll of quheit for four pund; the boll beir our pund, and much les in sum pairtes; and so the rest accordinglie. Bot immediatlie eftie this extraordiner rayne, the mercattis did ryse, for this unseasonable weddir pat mony in fear of dearth and famyne.

He adds (pp. 171-172) that "....About the fyftene day of *November* 1655, fell out ane great froast, and within few dayis thaireftir a storme and tempest of snow; and upone the tent day of December thaireftir, being ane Monounday, the storme increst and became so fearche and violent, the wind being at the north east, that in this so violent a storme thair perisched great numberis of schips, both in Scotland and England, and many hard by us heir at Mussilburgh, Newhavin, Bryntyland, and upone all the sea coistis both north and south. Great numberis of pepill, bestiall, and guidis perisched in this storme alsweill be sea as by land. The lyke storme wes not sene by the space of many yeiris befoir; no, not that great storme that did arryse at the death of King James the Sext did not equall this storme. This froast continued undissolvit fra the tent of November till the twenty day of December thaireftir, at quhilk tyme thair fell out a quyet and ane calme thow, without ony kynd of weit. There were great alteratioun of the pryces of victuell this yeir, the pryces in the foir end of the yeir being exceiding chaip, and chaiper nor in mony scoir of yeiris befoir; bot the weit and cold wethir, falling out in the spring and somer in great abundance, maid the mercatis to arryse to the triple and quadruple pryce and gif the money haid not bene skant, it haid bene far derar. Ceffis and excysis multiplyed, both upone menis persones and eftaites, as wes wonderfull.

1656 February 1656 is described by Nicholl (pp.174-189) as "...ane exceiding fair moneth, verry dry, warme, with a pleasant seasonable raine. The Spring this yeir wes very unko and unseasonable, be beffoun of the frequent frostis and rayne, exceiding much during the monethis of Marche and Apryll, quhilk the pepill of the cuntrey to fear famyn and dearth. The ministrie of the Presbytrie of Lothiane, taking this to thair consideratioun, did conclude a Fast to be keiped in the begynning of Maij; quihilk wes keipit in all the kirkis of this Presbytrie; and albeit with great waiknes, yit it wantit not the awin happy effect and blissing, for fra that day of humiliatioun the Lord did produce much fair and plesant weather for many dayis thaireftir following. This yeir 1656 producit abundance of bestiall, such as hors, nolt, scheip, and sum of these at ane verry easie pryce, albeit much death among the scheip this yeir. A guid mart kow wes fold for sextene pund, these bestiall being abundant and the money exceiding skant. Anent the fische this yeir, they wer also very plentifull. And albeit the West sea hering, this yeir and mony yeiris befoir, left thair awin loches, viz Lochfyne and Lochlong, yit they come into the river of Clyd, quhair in abundance thai wer takin and slayne, exceding fyne, great, and fresche; and continewit fresche and oppinlie sold very callor, almoist all winter, evin till mony dayis of Januar 1657. Thair wer also exceding great numberis of salmound and all uther soirt of fische takin and killed this yeir.

1657 Nicoll's diary entry for 1657 (pp. 201-8) notes that, "…At this tyme, and by the space of many yeirs of befoir, the Toun of Edinburgh wes destitute of watter to serve thair housis, and thair toun wellis wer dryed up, so that the inhabitantis could not be servite for want. The Toun, taking this to thair consideratioun, they concludit to dry the South loche, and to essay, gif the drying up of that loch micht help this evill. And for this end, they delt with the English sodgeris to cast trinsches about this loch, for gaddering the wattter thairto for the use of the Toun; quhilkes Englische sodgeris began thair wark upone the 3 day of August being Monday, the yeir of God 1657; and endit upone both sydes of the loch, befoir the twentie day of September, except a lytill parcell not above the lenth of a pair of buttes, quhilk wes left to be finiched and outred by fyve pure Scottis misterfull men for thair livelhood. The harvest was exceiding pleasant, and the cornes throw the haill natioun win and brocht in to the berne and berne yarid long befoir Michaelmes, and sum befoir the last of August, this yeir 1657. The victuell this yeir wes verrie guid, weill win, and very chaip. The somer being het and dry, and the harvest exceiding pleasant and airlie. All cornes for the maist pairt wer brocht in to the berne and berne yaird befoir the last of September this yeir.

1658 Nicoll (pp. 212-4) describes how "…this Februar 1658, and be the space of ane moneth and ane half befoir, viz the haill moneth of Januar, and half of December preceiding, wes exceiding seasonable, full of frost and snow; quhilk frost and snow dissolvit with ane calme thow, without weit or tempest, yit exceiding cold. Bot the moneth of Marche following, and much of Apryll wes bitter, and exceding scharp weather, mixt with frost, the wind continuing all that space in the eist and north eist. And farder, till the 20 day of Maij verrie cold weather. And farder, much cold weather thaireftir till the midst of Junij. This cold and unseasonable spring producit much diseases among the pepill through many parties of this natioun; speciallie of cold humoris upone the bodyes of wemen and men, quhairof few in the kingdome wer eximed. Besyde, that the cornes and gers wer far behind the ordiner tyme of growing; the wind still blowing out of the eist and benorth be the space of mony monethis. In the end of Maij 1658, fresche hering, great and fair, wer takin at Dumbar, and sold in the mercat and streitis of Edinburgh, quhilk we interpreit to be ominus, far by the cours of nature, and the cours of tyme and season of the yeir, the lyke nevir being sene of befoir.

Lamont (pp.110) describes how on December 16 "….Ther was a great tempest of raine and wynde, so that the waters increased exceidingly. That afternoone two ladds were drowned in that bourne that comes downe betuixt Hatton and Lundy; the one lived in Overpratous, and the other in Monthyriue, ther names were….Foggo …That afternoone, with others, they were comeing from a buriall that had beine att Largow chruch, and crossing the bridge ther, the trie being lowse, ther foote slipped, and fell in the water, so that these that were present could not recover them, because of the violence of the speate water, (for att this time ther was great abundance of snow on the grounde). Also, the same day, the sea overflowed some of its bankes, so that it bracke downe some houses in Buckheaven, also some standarts of the timber of the salt panns, both the Weyms and Kirkekaldie; also the waters marred diuers pairts of the high way betuixt Leuen and Kirkekaldie.

1659 John Nicholl (p.225-250) describes how at the start of this year, "...Thair wes in this moneth of Januar 1659, greatt and admirable tem pestis of wind, almoist throgh all this moneth, bot speciallie upone the 22 and 23 dayis of the same; quhairin the storme so increst upone the said 23, being ane Sonday, that the pepill in the Gray Freir kirk, being at sermond, wer forcit, all of thame and thair minister Mr Robert Traill, to flie out of the church for feir of their lyves. This tempest of wind continued mony dayis thaireftir. At this tyme, also, (*August and September*), thair fell out feirfull deluges and inundatiounes in Scotland, quhilk with thair effectis, sallbe noted in the end of the yeir.

That no sooner wes the viij d the pynt begun to be exactit, quhilk wes upone the first of September 1659, to the great hurt of the subectis, bot immediatlie thaireftir the Lord did manifest his anger in sending doun ane unhard and unkoth storme of wind and weit, be the space of thrie dayis and thrie nychtes, viz the secund, thrid, fourt, and fyft daysi of September, quhairby not onlie sindry housis in and upone the Watter of Leith, with ellevin myles belonging to Edinburgh, and fyve belonging to Heriotes Hospitall, with thair dammes, water-gangis, tymber and stone workis, the haill quheillis of thair myles, tymber graith, and haill uther warkes wer destroyed and violentlie takin away be these great diludges of watteris; bot lykewyse the haill tounes about sufferit the lyke dampnage, sik as Leith and Leith Harborie, Mussilburgh, Fifecherraw, Hadingtoun, Dalkeith, Leswaid, to the great admiratioun of many, evin of such persones as ar of greatest aige. So that the distressir and povertie of this natioun did still incres.

Lamont" (pp.117-8) records that on "...June 8 being Wedensday, ther was a great tempest of wynde all that day. In some places it brake tries, and blew up others by the roots; also ane English vessell, of ane indifferent burden, being laden with great salt, meade up hir towes (weighed anchor) in Leith rode, and came downe and perished at the harbour of the Ellie, bot the men (which were bot few, the rest being ashoare) were safe. Ane other vessell, comeing south with victuall, was forced to cast some of hir loadnen in the sea, by reason of the vehemency of the tempest, etc. On July 31, the communion was given att Largo, by Mr Ja. Makgill,...Also that Sabath night, and on Moneday, ther was a terribell tempest of rayne and wynde, so that bot a few were abell to come to the Monedays exercise, because the waters were not rydabell. In Lowthian, divers persons had mutch of ther corne sanded, by breaking foorth of the waters, especially these upon the water of Leith. The rains are again reported for August 1, "...being Moneday, and Sept. 5 being Moneday also, ther was great rains, which did great dammage in Lowthian to many poore peopell; bot specially upon the water of Leith, and the water of Elke at Dalkeith, many mills were throwen downe and spoyled, and mutch corne sanded. Nicoll describes how "...the late summer was generally very bad: in August and September, thair fell out feirfull deluges and inundations in Scotland'. He also describes the damage done by the gales of September 2nd, 3rd, 4th and 5th. Crops and 16 mills on the Leith were destroyed. Lamont, too, notes the 'great dammage upon the water of Leith, and the water of Eske at Dalkeith' caused by these storms.

References

John Lamont Diary of John Lamont of Newton 1649-1671 *National Library of Scotland, Maitland Club, 7*, pp.45-214.

John Nicoll A Diary of Public Transactions and other occurrences, chiefly in Scotland, 1650-1667 *National Library of Scotland, Bannatyne Club*, pp. 74-453.

BOOK REVIEW

Stirling Bridge & Falkirk 1297-98: William Wallace's rebellion. Pete Armstrong, illustrated by Angus McBride. Osprey Publishing. 96pp. ISBN 1 84176 510 4. £12.99.

With a strikingly illustrated cover akin to the author's *Bannockburn 1314* which we reviewed in FNH vol 25, this is a very readable presentation of two outsanding events, the stunningly victorious battle of Stirling Bridge, and the outstandingly disastrous battle of Falkirk. Osprey, Armstrong and the illustrators have made two eye-catching books to draw attention to these important events in Scotland's turbulant frustrating history, and to tempt the reader further into some of the many other treatments of the Wallace rebellion, academic, literary, popular, in print from the 15th century Fordun and Blind Harry, and on to the approaching commemorations of the 700th anniversary of his violent death in 2005.

GAINSBOROUGH'S BEAUTIFUL MRS GRAHAM
(Mary Cathcart of Schaw Park, Alloa)

Helen Smailes

In the early summer of 2003 the National Gallery of Scotland mounted a fascinating exhibition devoted to the Gallery's world-famous portrait of *The Honble Mrs Graham* by Thomas Gainsborough (1727-1788) (Figure 1), one of the finest and most sensitive British portrait painters of the eighteenth century. Since the picture entered the Gallery in 1859 as part of the foundation collection, it has become established as an international icon for the National Galleries of Scotland collectively. This exhibition, curated for the Gallery by Hugh Belsey, a recognised authority on the artist and curator of Gainsborough's House in Sudbury, explored the personal, social and historical context of the picture in depth for the first time. The exhibition in Edinburgh followed immediately after a major exhibition on Gainsborough at Tate Britain which also travelled to the United States. 2003 has therefore become the year of Thomas Gainsborough on an international scale.

Mary Graham (1757-1792) was the second of the four daughters of Charles Schaw Cathcart, 9th Lord Cathcart of Schaw Park. Lord Cathcart, a major patron of the Scottish portrait painter David Allan of Alloa (1744-1796) (Figure 2), pursued a distinguished military career before being appointed Ambassador-Extraordinary to the court of Catherine the Great in St Petersburg in 1768. In 1774, on their return to Britain, Mary Cathcart and her elder sister Jane, Maid-of-Honour to the Queen, celebrated a double wedding to the Perthshire laird Thomas Graham of Balgowan and the 4th Duke of Atholl respectively. The following year the third daughter Louisa was to make an equally prestigious marriage to the eminent statesman the 7th Viscount Stormont, later 2nd Earl of Mansfield.

As an exquisite society beauty, Mary Graham sat to Gainsborough for at least three portraits all of which, including her "fancy" portrait in the guise of a housemaid (Tate Britain), featured in the National Gallery's exhibition. In 1777 the full-length now in the Gallery's collection was much acclaimed at the annual exhibition of the Royal Academy to which Gainsborough had contributed no fewer than eight pictures after a five year absence from public exhibitions. In this "compleatest of all pictures" the newly married Mary Graham is portrayed in Van Dyck dress, a fashion well-established by the 1770s and which was intended to place her portrait within the great tradition of British court portraiture of the seventeenth century. Gainsborough used as his compositional model for the picture a magnificent full-length Van Dyck of the Countess of Chesterfield, also shown in the exhibition.

Mary Graham's premature death from tuberculosis, or 'consumption' in 1792 left her husband devastated. From 1794, when he raised the 'Perthshire Volunteers', Thomas Graham sought distraction through an army career, not only to distract himself from grief, but as part of the wider response to the perceived threat of

French invasion. After serving with Wellington in the Peninsula, he was promoted general and, in 1814, raised to the peerage as Lord Lynedoch – a distinction commemorated in several imposing portraits by Sir Thomas Lawrence and of which the most dramatic was lent to the exhibition by Perth Museum and Art Gallery (Figure 3). In the meantime, being unable to bear the contemplation of his late wife's portrait, Thomas Graham had the Gainsborough despatched to Kenwood House, Hampstead where it was entrusted to Mary's favourite sister Louisa, Countess of Mansfield. Several years later the painting was placed in the custody of a London-based firm of art dealers for the remainder of Graham's life. Some time after his death in 1843, the full-length Gainsborough was rediscovered by Lord Lynedoch's cousin and heir Robert Graham of Redgorton, almost eighty years after Mary Graham had first sat to Gainsborough. Captivated by its exceptional quality, Graham of Redgorton paid a thousand guineas to secure the picture from his cousin's estate for eventual presentation to the Scottish nation.

Following this sensational turn of events, the Gainsborough re-emerged into the public domain in 1857 at the great Manchester Art Treasures exhibition where it was hung with *The Blue Boy*, then in the collection of the Duke of Westminster, and attracted crowds of admirers from the opening day. In 1859, when the new National Gallery of Scotland opened to the public, Robert Graham bequeathed his most precious family heirloom to the Scottish nation on condition that the picture would never leave Edinburgh. At the Gallery the Gainsborough has continued to exercise its original fascination for almost 150 years. Its popularity has been echoed in the composition of later portraits such as *Clarissa* by Sir John Everett Millais and it has generated a whole industry of souvenir production focussed upon *The Honble Mrs Graham*. The exhibition explored this extraordinary afterlife of the portrait and of Gainsborough's reputation in general and included one of the most memorable examples of this self-perpetuating cult – a promotional poster for Maidenform lingerie designed in 1956, based directly upon the portrait and bearing the slogan "I dreamed I was a Work of Art in my Maidenform bra"!

The exhibition secured the co-operation of major museum and gallery lenders including Tate Britain, the Victoria and Albert Museum and the National Museum of Scotland. In addition the Gallery obtained the support of several private owners most of whom possess Cathcart and Graham family pictures which have never been seen in public. Comprising a total of about eighty loans, the exhibition *Gainsborough's Beautiful Mrs Graham* brought together for the first time a range of great works by Gainsborough, Reynolds, Lawrence and van Dyck, and poignant family memorabilia including items of costume and personal letters associated with Mary Graham and husband Lord Lynedoch. The exhibition as a whole provided unique insights into the social and cultural life of three distinguished Scottish families in late eighteenth-century Scotland, London and Europe and a fascinating study of their patronage of Gainsborough, Reynolds, Romney and David Allan.

Reference

Gainsborough's Beautiful Mrs Graham. Hugh Belsey. National Gallery of Scotland. 62 pp. 2003. ISBN 1 903278 38 4. £9.95. The Companion book of the Exhibition. Available plus postage from the National Gallery of Scotland, Retail Department, Dean Gallery, Belford Road, Edinburgh EH14 3DS, or by personal visit to the National Gallery of Scotland shop.

Illustrations
1. Thomas Gainsborough *The Honble Mrs Graham*. 1775. National Gallery of Scotland.
2. David Allan, *The Family of the 9th Lord Cathcart*. 1765. National Gallery of Scotland.
3. Sir Thomas Lawrence, *Lord Lynedoch*. 1815. Perth Museum and Art Gallery.

Illustrations 1 and 2 are by courtesy of the National Galleries of Scotland, and 3 of the Perth Museum and Art Gallery.

The author Helen Smailes (a *Forth Naturalist and Historian* reader) is Senior Curator of British Art at the National Gallery of Scotland, and acted as administrative curator for the Edinburgh exhibition 4 April to 22 June 2003.

Figure 1 The Honble Mrs Graham.

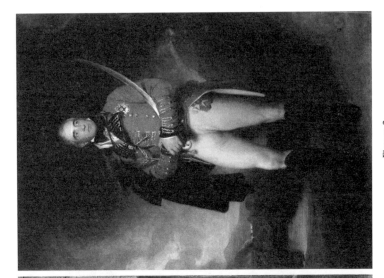

Figure 3
Thomas Graham, Lord Lynedoch.

Figure 2
The Cathcart family.

EARLY HISTORIC (DARK AGE) STIRLING:
WAS THE GOWAN HILL BEDE'S *GIUDI?*

Ron Page

Introduction

Historians have found no record of the place-name Stirling before the town was given Royal Burgh status in 1124 by David I. Yet the town must have been long established to be among the earliest of the Royal Burghs of Scotland – others were Perth, Edinburgh, Roxburgh, Dunfermline, and Berwick. We would expect the origins of these burghs to go back into the Dark Age. This period has been so-called because we have very little by way of documentary records for it. Unfortunately this is especially so for what is now Scotland, where there are no indigenous records for the period, and we have to rely on documents from elsewhere and on archaeological evidence. One valuable source is the Venerable Bede's *History of the English Church and People*, written in 731 AD, which has one or two references to North Britain and the Picts and Scots. One of these mentions the town of *Giudi*. We have no native source to throw light on the location of Bede's *urbs Giudi*, but there are a few references in certain Irish *Annals* and in the *Anglo-Saxon Chronicle* to support inferences that may be drawn from Bede's *History*. It is possible, however, to supplement documentary evidence by judicious use of archaeological discoveries to increase our understanding of Early Historic Scotland.

In the *History of the English Church and People* (1968, Penguin edn., p 51) Bede, describing North Britain, said 'For many years this region suffered attacks from two savage extraneous races, Scots from the northwest, and Picts from the north. I term these races extraneous, not because they came from outside Britain, but because their lands were sundered from that of the Britons: for two sea estuaries lay between, one of which runs broad and deep into the country from the sea to the east and the other from the west, although they do not actually meet. In the middle of the eastern estuary stands the city of *Giudi*, …'.

The attacks on north Britain as described by Bede were a continuation of the attacks by the northern tribes five hundred years earlier against the Romans. The two main tribes (or confederations of tribes) were the Caledonians and the Meatae. The Meatae were described by the Roman historian Cassius Dio as living 'close by the wall which divides the island in two, and the Caledonians live beyond them'. Unfortunately we do not know whether Hadrian's Wall or the Antonine Wall was meant. It was probably the latter, since the Meatae have left traces of their name both 5 km to the north-east of Stirling at the hill-fort of Dumyat and 12 km to the south at the hill-fort of Myot Hill.

These hill-forts are usually regarded as typical Iron Age edifices. They may have been constructed several centuries before the Roman period, as far back as the eighth century BC. Some appear to have been abandoned before the Roman invasion, but few have been accurately dated. Some certainly existed during the Roman period, and continued beyond that into the so-called Dark Ages, perhaps being re-occupied and partly reconstructed. Indeed, as Feachem pointed out (1977, 24), the Roman period was merely a temporary interruption in the life of Iron Age Britain. Especially in north Britain the Iron Age gradually developed into the Dark Age. Since Bede and the Annalists wrote of it, even if sketchily, it is better termed the Early Historic period.

Recently a new flood lighting system for the Wallace Monument was inserted through the rampart of the Abbey Craig hill-fort near Stirling (described as Iron Age in RCAHMS 1963, Fig. 4 and No 69, p. 71). This rampart was found to be timber-laced (Glendinning, 2001) and charcoal samples from the burnt timbers were found to have radiocarbon dates calibrated to AD 500-700 and 590-780 (Lorna Main, Stirling Council Archaeologist, pers. comm.). This determination of dates places this small hill-fort firmly in the Early Historic period, and renews interest in that period for this part of Scotland.

The striking absence of information about the Stirling area for those times was the subject of comment by Graham (1959, 63), whose remarks can hardly be improved upon –

'Nobody who considers the map of Dark Age Scotland can fail to be puzzled by the absence from it of Stirling. The Castle Rock of Stirling is ideally suited to primitive methods of defence, and its command of the point where the north-going Roman road crossed the Forth must already in the post-Roman centuries have given it the strategic importance that it retained until 1746. It also overlooks the head of navigation of the river. On all these grounds some record of Dark Age Stirling might reasonably have been looked for – to set, for example, beside Din Eidyn, Alclud, Dunpelder, Dunadd, Dunollie, or Brude's *munitio* in the north – but so far none has been forthcoming. The purpose of this note is to suggest that Bede's *urbs Giudi* should fill the blank'. (Graham, writing for specialists, took it for granted that his readers would recognise Din Eidyn as Edinburgh, Alclud as Dumbarton Rock, Dunadd as the capital of Dalriada, etc. Details of these sites may be found in Feachem, 1977).

One obstacle to the recognition of *Giudi* as Stirling is the absence of visible traces of early fortifications beneath the castle. The buildings of the castle are extensive, occupying the greater part of the Castle Rock. There is, of course, no knowing what may be revealed when, if ever, excavation in that area becomes possible. To the east of the Castle, however, lies the Gowan Hill (gowan may equal daisy, but other interpretations of this place name are possible), with the Mote Hill (RCAHMS 1963, No 80, p 79) on its north-east corner – Figure 1a.

Feachem (1977, 118) considered that although no remains of a prehistoric fort had been recorded at Dumbarton Rock nevertheless the *oppidum* (chief town) of the Strathclyde Britons, and earlier that of the Damnonii, (one of the native tribes named on the map of Roman times by Ptolemy) had been there. He continued '… it is reasonably certain that here, *as at the comparable site in Stirling*, (author's italics) such a fort existed'.

Report

In 1995 Digney, a student from Stirling, studying archaeology at York University, recognised a number of unrecorded features, earth and stone banks on the Gowan Hill, (an area of approximately 4.5 hectares), and suggested that these might be the defences of an Iron Age fort, or *oppidum* (Figure 1b).

The area of between 2 and 3 hectares enclosed by banks shown in Figure 1b, together with the area below the buildings of the Castle itself, exceeds the area available at Dumbarton Rock, the *Alt Clut* of the Dumnonii. Could this be the *oppidum* or an *oppidum* of the Meatae? Neither Dumyat or Myot Hill compare in size with Traprain Law (16 hectares) in East Lothian, which Feachem (1977, 120) proposed as the *oppidum* of the Votidinii, or Eildon Hill North (also 16 hectares) near Melrose in Roxburghshire, suggested as the *oppidum* of the Selgovae (Feachem 1977, 150). A powerful tribe like the Meatae would be expected to have an *oppidum* of some considerable size.

Figure 2, depicting a section across the Gowan Hill and the position of Stirling Castle, shows how suitable this site would be. Clearance of gorse, bushes and brambles etc., of three strips down the steep north-east facing slope of the area revealed a series of what were apparently traces of banks. No ditches were seen, but presence or absence of these would only be revealed by excavation. As modern surveying equipment was not available to us, the author and Stephen Digney surveyed these by stretching cords tightly up the slopes, measuring the slope of the cord by clinometer, and its direction by prismatic compass, then dropping a plumb line at 1 metre intervals along the cord to measure the distance from the cord to the ground surface. Where necessary intervals smaller than 1 metre were used. By plotting the results, representing the cord by the hypotenuse of a triangle of the appropriate angle, the three profiles shown in Figure 3 were obtained. The banks can be followed along the slope between these profiles and beyond, but the thick vegetation makes this difficult. The banks on the western side of the Gowan Hill are more easily accessible. The approximate position of these is indicated in Figure 1b.

These findings were reported in *Discovery and Excavation in Scotland*, (Digney, 1995, 16), but without illustration.

Discussion

Skene in the nineteenth century identified *Giudi* with the island of Inchkeith, on the grounds that 'in the middle' of the Firth of Forth meant literally in the midst of the sea. This seems an unlikely situation for an important town of that time.

Hunter Blair (1947, 27-8) suggested that rather than the identification of *urbs Giudi* with Inchkeith as proposed by Skene (which is still adopted in the Penguin revised edition of Bede's *History of the English Church and People*, 1968, p 51), it could be either Cramond or Inveresk. Professor Jackson (1964, 36-8) disputed this, and decisively supported Graham's view that Stirling represents *urbs Giudi*. The identification was accepted by the Ordnance Survey for their map *Britain in the Dark Ages*, 2nd edn., 1966, and by Professor Duncan (1975, 61) – '... *urbs Iudeu*, pretty certainly a fort on Stirling rock'. (*Iudeu* and *Giudi* are evidently alternative forms of the same name – see Note below). Jackson (1981, 1-7) returned to the question to refute the suggestions of Hunter Blair, and after thoroughly discussing the problem concluded that beyond reasonable doubt Stirling was the location of Bede's *urbs Giudi*. Alcock (1981, 176) cautiously agreed – 'If *Giudi* was indeed located at Stirling, then clearly *urbs Giudi* must be Stirling Castle Rock'. Alcock reserved judgement because no traces of early fortifications have yet been found beneath the medieval and later castle. The discovery of traces of banks on the Gowan Hill, between the Castle Rock and the Mote Hill, suggests that a sizeable settlement, perhaps an *oppidum* existed there. Several banks on the north-eastern slope would seem to indicate that this was not merely a cattle enclosure – that would require only a single bank and ditch, or a simple palisade. These banks need to be excavated, to ensure that they are not natural features. Excavation might yield dating material, and should show whether or not there were ditches associated with them. Usually banks are produced from the up-cast of their accompanying ditches. It is perhaps too much to hope that excavations on the summit of the hill would reveal traces of structures. The soil cover of the rock is very thin, and has been subject over the ages to a great deal of disturbance.

The presence of traces of fortifications, probably Iron Age or Dark Age, perhaps both, do not in themselves provide evidence for *urbs Giudi*, but they do strengthen the argument for an important settlement beside the Mote Hill. That place name itself, meaning the meeting place of the moot or council, is a significant feature. In conjunction with consideration of the geographic situation outlined by Graham (1959, 63) the case for *urbs Giudi* being the precursor of Stirling is greatly strengthened.

Acknowledgements

The discovery of the banks on the Gowan Hill, and the recognition of their significance as an indication of an unrecognised hill-fort, was the work of Stephen Digney. Clearance of the strips down the north-east slope of the hill was assisted by Eric Ross, Paul Millar and the late Andrew Conoboy. Permission for the clearances was kindly given on behalf of the Stirling Council by Tim Dixon of Environmental Services.

I thank Stephen Digney for useful comments on a draft of this paper, and I have attempted to remove some of the obscurities pointed out by the editors. The opinions and the remaining errors are my own.

Note

Jackson (1964, 37) explained that Bede's *Giudi* 'looks like an attempt to spell *Iudeu*; the G means the sound of Y in English Yes, as does I of *Iudeu*; the only real difference is in the -i in Bede's form, which could be scribal corruption, or misinformation.' The identification of *Giudi* and *Iudeu* with Stirling referred to in the Introduction above, is reinforced by the observation of Chadwick (1963,

159, note 1) that 'tra merin Iodo' from *Gododdin*, 1209, means 'beyond the sea of *Iudeu*' (i.e., the Firth of Forth).

The discussions regarding *Giudi* and *Iudeu* have not previously made the connection with *Niuduera*, which is another form of the same name. Saint Cuthbert went from Melrose '*ad terram Pictorum ubi dicitur Niuduera regio*' (to the land of the Picts, called *Niuduera*); (Two Lives of Cuthbert, ed. B Colgrove, p 82, quoted by Stenton, (1971, 87). This must obviously refer to his crossing the Firth of Forth, and the *Book of Lecan*, fo.43 bb, quoted by Anderson (1990, 127) refers to Saint Serf possessing Culross '*itir sliab n-Ochel acus muir n-Guidan*' – between the Ochil Hills and the Firth of Forth. These and a quotation from an eighth-century poem, *Miracula Nynie Episcopi*, corrected by Levison to read '*Pictoram nationes quae Niduarae dicuntur*' (to the nation of the Picts called *Niduarae*) were used by Wainwright (1955, 42-3) to show that the 'Picts of Galloway' were a twelfth-century myth based on confusing *Niduari* with 'of Nithsdale'. He made no reference, however, to *Giudi* and *Iudeu* and Stirling. His case would have been strengthened had he done so.

References

Alcock, L. (1981). Early historic fortifications in Scotland. In *Hill-Fort Studies* (ed. G. Guilbert), pp 150-180. Leicester.

Anderson, A. O. (1922). *Early Sources of Scottish History, A.D. 500 to 1286.* 1990 edn., with corrections by M. Anderson. Stamford.

Bede, A History of the English Church and People. Penguin Classics, 1968 edn. Translated by Sherley-Price, revised by Latham.

Chadwick, N. K. (1963). The Conversion of Northumbria. In *Celt and Saxon; Studies in the Early British Border.* (ed. N. K. Chadwick) pp138-166. Cambridge University Press.

Digney, S. (1995). Gowan Hill: Enclosure (Oppidum?) *Discovery and Excavation in Scotland,* 16.

Duncan, A. A. M. (1975). Scotland: the Making of the Kingdom. Edinburgh University Press.

Feachem, R. (1977). Guide to Prehistoric Scotland. London: Batsford.

Glendinning, B. (2001). Wallace Monument Replacement Floodlighting, *Discovery and Excavation in Scotland,* 2, (New Series), 97.

Graham, A. (1959). Giudi, *Antiquity* 33, 63-65.

Hunter Blair, P. (1947). The Origins of Northumbria, *Archaeologia Aeliana,* 4th series, 25.

Jackson, K. H. (1964). 'On the Northern British Section in Nennius', In *Celt and Saxon: Studies in the Early British Border* (ed. N. K. Chadwick) pp. 20-62. Cambridge University Press.

Jackson, K. H. (1981). 'Varia: I. Bede's *urbs Giudi*: Stirling or Cramond?', *Cambridge Medieval Celtic Studies,* 2, 1-7.

RCAHMS. (Royal Commission on the Ancient and Historic Monuments of Scotland). (1963). *An Inventory of the Ancient and Historic Monuments of Stirlingshire.*

Stenton, F. M. (1971). *Anglo-Saxon England,* 3rd edn. Oxford University Press.

Wainwright, F. T. (1955). 'The Picts and the Problem' In *The Problem of the Picts* (ed. F. T. Wainwright) pp 1-53, Nelson.

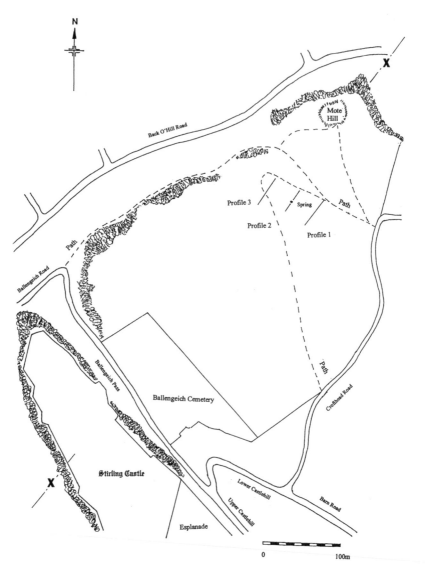

Figure 1a. Present day Gowan Hill, with Stirling Castle and the Mote Hill.

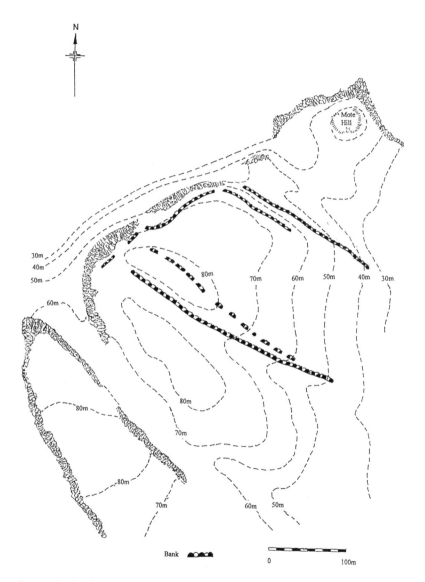

Figure 1b. Banks detected on Gowan Hill, approximate positions. (After Digney, unpublished, pers. comm., 1995).

These banks vary in width and form, and may be of different dates. The two banks shown on the NE are only to illustrate the rough position; there are in fact more than two – see Figure 3. The broken line on the SW is not certainly an artificial bank, it may be a natural feature.

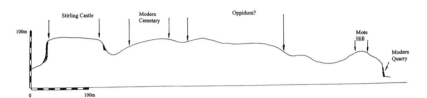

Figure 2. Section XX in Figure 1a, across Gowan Hill and Castle rock.

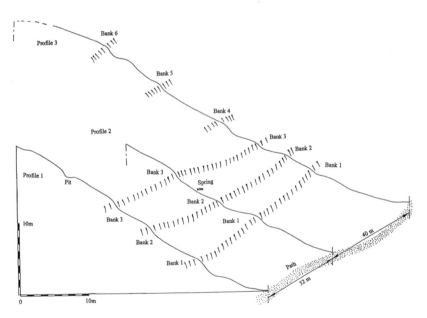

Figure 3. Profiles of banks on NE slope of Gowan Hill.

HEAVY METAL MINES IN THE OCHILS:
CHRONOLOGY AND CONTEXT

John G. Harrison

Introduction

This is an outline of documentary research carried out during 2001 into the heavy metal mines of the Ochils. A longer and more fully referenced version is available (1). The documents do not name the sites consistently but, so far as possible, Table 1 identifies documented sites with the known remains of mine workings.

Chronology of the Ochils Mines

There is no confirmation of the tradition that copper from Mine Wood, Bridge of Allan, was used for 'bawbees' in the late sixteenth century and I have found no record of mines in the Ochils before 1607 when William Alexander, later earl of Stirling, was granted the minerals of Menstrie. A note written by James Wright of Loss in 1763 refers to 'the Earl of Stirling's copper mines near Menstry'. Other possible 17th century sites are hinted at by a mid century mention of a copper mine at 'Airthrey' where the ore also contained silver and gold and another site 'Eastward of Aithree, amongst the Ochels upon the water of Alquharey [Auld Wharry], within two miles of the head of the water' where there was copper ore. And a contract for work at 'Airthrey' dated 1714 refers to the place where 'the mines were formerlie wrought'.

But the 18th century was to be the heyday of the Ochils mines. The discovery of a vein of silver at Alva in about 1714 initially brought rich rewards and was clearly the trigger for a number of speculative searches. All the proprietors hoped to find silver – though in the event they were fortunate if even copper was found in economic quantities. Known finds of other metals will be explicitly mentioned in this paper; otherwise it can be assumed that the product, if any, was copper. The Alva discovery, at a time when silver supplies from other sources were curtailed by war, persuaded the government to allow the return of the exiled Jacobite proprietor, Sir John Erskine of Alva, to assist with exploiting the seam. Erskine had widespread interests in other mines and mineral works, so far afield as Guernsey, the Isle of Man and Coll, but also at Linlithgow, Leadhills and more locally at Blairlogie. A key figure in this early phase was Daniel Peck. Henry Kalmeter, a Swedish mining expert who visited Alva in 1719 states that Peck was involved with Sir Charles Erskine at Linlithgow. He expands on this:

> *An Englishman called Peck, who came to Scotland to look for metals in several places, had in 1714 taken the opportunity of a narrow strip of white sparr, or rock, running up right across a high mountain, to go in there prospecting, and when he had hardly come one yard, a gland of silver was discovered which was not only rich*

in itself but also contained pieces or lumps of solid silver which I have seen myself ...

Peck seems to have originated in Cheshire but by 1715 Mr Daniel Peck 'of London' was involved with the local laird Dundas of Manor and John Adair, the geographer in the mines at 'Airthrey'. After this partnership was dissolved, Peck entered into another agreement with Dundas and two other local lairds to develop the 'Airthrey' mines. These contracts could refer to either Bridge of Allan or Logie. Peck was also involved in various Scots salt and coal mining and shipping ventures and in 1727 appears as Daniel Peck, Esquire, of Linlithgow.

Kalmeter, an intelligent, well-informed observer, is unequivocal that it was the discovery at Alva which stimulated a burst of prospecting – and equally clear that by 1719, though work continued at Alva, nothing was being produced. By this time, however, there were mines and investigations at or close to Menstrie, on the laird of Manor's lands (*i.e.* 'Airthrey') and at Blairlogie. Sir Charles Erskine was the dominant partner in the Blairlogie mines by this time and remained so until he sold or assigned his interest in 1729. Evidently one of the mines which Kalmeter saw was a preliminary investigation at Loss. Several draft contracts survive for Loss over the next few years, involving many Scots lairds and others, such as Hope of Rankeillor and Bethune of Blebo, men well-known for their mining interests. Simultaneous agreements and explorations were taking place on land belonging to Stirling of Keir (probably Cauldhame and Glen Tye at this stage), Linton of Pendreich and Stewart of Tillicoultry as well as at Loss in Menstrie Glen. The various lairds often had shares in each others mines and sought advice from anywhere it could be had. There is little indication of how successful these ventures were. In 1726, John Hewetson granted a receipt to James Wright of Loss for eleven score and six stone of ore, removed 'to Holland and London for tryal'; years later Wright's grandson (also James Wright of Loss) would claim that several tons of ore had been removed during his grandfather's time. The following year, work at Loss lapsed until 1730 or 1731 when it was fleetingly revived and lapsed again until 1745 when a Mr Thomas Jones inspected the mines of Pendreich, Loss, Tillicoultry and Logie and entered into draft agreements with at least some of the proprietors. Work at Tillicoultry may even have continued into the 1750s as in 1772 John Drysdale recalled that some English miners had lived in Tillicoultry but had gone away about 20 years before and the Old Statistical Account for the parish puts the Tillicoultry copper mines 'near 50 years' before 1792 when a 'company of gentlemen at London' were the tacksmen, and for several years employed about 50 men. A draft tack of the Pendreich mines to Thomas Vangen and Company is dated 1749.

A Memorandum dated 1753 notes 15 sites on or close to the Alva estate where work had been carried out in the past or where ore was thought to exist (2). And, in November 1753, John Sickler, former agent to the Tillicoultry copper mines, proposed to the young James Wright, current laird of Loss, that if he was allowed six months to find suitable partners to provide finance, he was willing to take a 31 year lease of the Loss mines. A provisional agreement resulted in some work within days of the original proposal and by early December Wright had got a copy of Mr Jones's tack of the Blairlogie mines from his neighbour, the laird of Manor. Between January and May 1754 more contracts were drafted between Wright and Sickler and his partners, now revealed as the original 'partners and adventurers' in the former Tillicoultry company and who included a Robert Wilson. But again work seems to have lapsed quite quickly. By August 1756, Wright had made out a draft advertisement for his mines.

Wright's excitement presaged a more widespread resumption of activity. By May 1757 the Alva mines had been inspected by John Williamson who, by March 1758 had been taken on to supervise resumed work at Alva; the old workings were cleared out and work continued through all or much of 1758. In early 1759 the chemist Joseph Black confirmed the presence of cobalt in the Alva ore. Despite an approach from Dr Roebuck of the Carron Company, Erskine of Alva himself formed a company with wide contacts and employing considerable expertise to work the eastern side of Alva. That company was to continue seriously at Alva till about 1766, cobalt probably being the main product. However, other minerals were found and, though less important, were exploited. In 1759 The Company for Smelting Lead from Coal had inspected the Alva sites but noted that the rock was hard, there were problems with water and, in spite of numerous trials, the appearance was not good and they saw no encouragement in view of the current low price of lead. In spite of that the lead vein was explored and is occasionally mentioned over the next few years.

In September 1762 John Williamson reported that there were four veins working at Alva, as well as the air-shaft at 'Carnachan' *i.e.* at the Carnaughton Burn, west of Alva. Carnaughton is mentioned intermittently thereafter. In 1770 the Carron Company expressed mild interest in Carnaughton but in 1771 they regretted to hear that Carnaughton had been abandoned due to barrenness and it then vanishes from the record.

Meanwhile, the late 1750s and early 1760s saw further, transient prospecting at Loss, Knockhill (part of the Keir estate) and Blairlogie. In late 1761, Messrs Patten and Richardson became involved at Loss and Alva and their contacts with James Wright of Loss generated a good deal of correspondence. But their interest quickly waned and work at Loss was abandoned in late 1763. However, by that time, two further local ventures were being planned, at Logie and at the western end of the Airthrey estate, modern Bridge of Allan. The Logie mine had been included in a 1745 contract with Dundas of Manor. But about 1762 James Wright of Loss formed a partnership with Mr Charles Freebairn, architect in Edinburgh, to exploit the Logie mine, which they rented from Mayne of Powhouse. It is marked on a sketch plan concerning a contemporary agreement between Wright and Mayne about other matters (3). In an enthusiastic letter dated 1 February 1762 Freebairn tells Wright that he has already 'engaged Wilson to procure miners and oversee them work not according to his own opinion but expressly by mine'. Work began in February and was to continue, at least intermittently, until February 1765 though by that time the correspondence was a great deal colder and more formal. Work resumed in April 1766 but now with only two miners and continued intermittently through 1766 and 1767 in spite of a Report by Mr Williamson in 1766 that the prospects for Logie were 'not propitious'. Probably work stopped after November 1767.

At Bridge of Allan the story is more complex and good deal longer and is the likely source of the story of another Ochils silver mine – though it is unlikely that anything other than copper was produced in economic quantities. Haldane of Airthrey, the proprietor, was in contact with the Erskines of Alva and in one of his first letters to Erskine, Nicholas Crisp – a partner and a technical adviser to the Alva cobalt mine – says that the delay in hearing from Haldane has left him no choice but to write into Cornwall. By November 1761 he reported that he had found a man in Cornwall who would examine the veins and on 12 December 1761, George Cockburn in Edinburgh told James Wright (of Loss) that 'Mr William Philips, a miner from Cornwall, sent down by Mr Crisp' was now ready to inspect Haldane's mines. As Haldane was not available, he asks Wright (as someone in Haldane's trust) to assist (4). An undated draft letter in James Wright's hand clearly follows this visit of inspection (5); he and Philips, and a man called Russell who had previously been one of the miners, had found the site full of rubbish. But Philips seemed 'exceedingly pleased with them and expects they will turn out well'. Samples were to be sent to Crisp and 'Williamson' had suggested that miners could be diverted from Alva to Airthrey. On 19 February 1762 James Erskine (of Alva) wrote to Crisp congratulating him on the appearance at Airthrey 'I think there is appearance of very good copper to be easily got. The people who formerly wrought there seem to have been very ignorant believing nothing was copper but the purple, red and green ores whereas the white, gray and black horny ores are frequent in these hills'.

By May 1762 Crisp reported a small quantity of silver present in the copper at Logie. And in August Haldane wrote to Erskine that 'Ten Great Lairds' were involved in discussions of metallurgy 'in hopes of extracting riches from the hidden recesses of the hills,' adding, with a wise caution he was later to lose, that 'it will be well if eight of the ten are not disappointed'. By the following spring a hopeful report claimed that there would be 50 to 60 tons of Airthrey ore ready by the summer; the letter is not explicit but this seems to have been the ore which generated the 'silver mine' myth. The writer would rather sell at the mine though it was actually being taken to Leith in barrels. In late July 1763 Crisp reported on an analysis of the Airthrey ore – and his letter was copied both to Erskine and to Wright of Loss. During August he reported excitedly to Haldane that he was achieving significant silver yields from the Airthrey ore and on 24th August 'here is treasure almost beyond belief if you can get it out in a large way' (6). Later reports of a local silver mine are based on a comment in the Old Statistical Account for Logie parish that between 1761 and 1764 'a company of gentlemen from England, along with the proprietor got about 50 barrels of silver ore'. The venture is said to have collapsed when the consignee in London went bankrupt – probably referring to Crisp (7). The OSA can only refer to Bridge of Allan as the proprietor is named as Haldane of Airthrey whilst the Logie proprietor was Mayne; the writer is not likely to have confused them as he was a cousin and the eventual heir of James Wright of Loss, exploiter of the Logie mine, and they were frequent correspondents during the period.

In July 1764 Haldane of Airthrey obtained a charter under the Great Seal of all the gold, silver, lead and copper ores and other metals in the barony of Haldane, lands of Airthrey and all his other lands (8). Almost immediately, if the reduction in documentation is to be trusted (and consistent with the OSA story) the veins began to yield less. But some sort of work continued and 1770 provides a key document, the Report on the Mines of the Wester Airthrey Company, made by John Williamson and dated 26 September (9). This Report describes the New Level or Cross Cut, driven from the level of the carse, six feet high and four wide 'being two hundred and twenty seven fathoms three feet [416 metres], so straight that one may stand at the entrance of it, and see a candle burning at the place where the cross-cut flanks the east and west vein'. This description leaves no doubt that this is the drainage level at Bridge of Allan. Other circumstances of the Report and personnel show that this was the mine which Philips had inspected and Crisp had so excitedly discussed. However, Williamson concludes ambiguously:

> it is difficult, nay Impossible for any man to give an opinion with regard to success or otherwise in any mining tryal. How often have we seen the most flattering appearances proves nothing, and those of a less promising aspect turn to good account? But ...there is now all the reason the nature of these adventures will admit of, to hope the best...

Later that year, Alexander Sheriff noted that the accounts of the undertaking were very clear and 'satisfactory in everything except the success of the undertaking, which no man can help'. Work seemingly continued and some copper was still being removed and sold. In February 1773 Haldane was hoping to keep the venture going, to interest new partners or to assign the lease as the only hope of retrieving the partners' losses and he so far succeeded that in 1775 some work continued. On 12 March 1779 Haldane wrote, sadly, from the Airthrey Mine House (at Bridge of Allan) that 'all here is in great confusion. There is a large bing lying on the floor, twice the quantity that is in the casks'. He sends a sample for Dr [Joseph] Black to examine, adding, desperately that at least something should be done to sell off what was there (10). Work was resumed at Bridge of Allan in 1800 but was again abandoned in 1807.

The personnel

Most of the people involved in these mines had their counterparts in the contemporary Scots lead industry whilst some men involved in the Ochils were also interested in lead. Scots partners in the Alva Cobalt venture included various merchants, two lawyers, the cashier of the Royal Bank of Scotland, perhaps acting for the bank itself and Alexander Sheriff, a Leith merchant, deeply involved in the Scots lead industry. He was evidently one of the first people consulted by Erskine of Alva in 1759, partly on account of his technical expertise. It was he who first drew a comparison with the ores of the Hartz mountains. He was involved with Bridge of Allan from1762 until 1775, drawing in Nicolas Crisp and other experts and he did a good deal of the business administration for Bridge of Allan and Alva.

Local lairds generally invested in mines on their own lands and less consistently in those of their neighbours. But they always went in as partners rather than as sole proprietors. In 1763, James Wright of Loss had shares in the mines of (amongst others) Loss, the west side of Alva, Keir and Blairlogie. The 1715 contract involving Dundas of Manor, Daniel Peck and John Adair was unusual in not involving other lairds. The meeting of 'ten great lairds' discussing metallurgy was clearly only one of many such excited gatherings. Ayton of Blebo and the Hopes of Rankeillor had more wide ranging interests. Henry Kalmeter visited Rankeillor several times and comments wryly on Hope's vain excitement at the potential mineral wealth of his own estate. The Erskines of Alva were involved in mines in Scotland and beyond over two generations. James Wright of Loss had at least a transient interest in the Tyndrum lead mines as well as in iron mines at Tillicoultry, coal mines in the Forth Valley and other aspects of mineral exploitation in Scotland. In many cases the mine-owners involved their wider families.

Technicians (or even scientists) were also involved and some invested capital, too. Nicholas Crisp was a potter, an analytical chemist and also an investor; his contribution has been considered by Turnbull. Daniel Peck also had both technical skills and capital to invest. John Adair, the geographer involved in the 1715 attempt, probably at Logie, is not otherwise known to have been involved in mining and, given his long and often despairing efforts to gain recognition and payment for his cartographic work it is surprising that he had any spare capital to invest. Louis Baden and John Sickler are other men who laid claim to some mining expertise and capital.

Charles Freebairn, Wright's partner in the Logie mine between 1763 and 1766, described himself as 'architect in Edinburgh'. He was the son of James Freebairn, a teacher of French in Edinburgh. His only recorded architectural work (at Abercairny House, Perthshire between 1755-9 and at Innerpeffray Library, Muthill, Perthshire 1758-1762) put him both geographically and socially close to Wright of Loss, who had family ties with southern Perthshire (11). Wright and Freebairn were 'equally concerned' in the Logie mine but though Freebairn was the 'expert', Robert Wilson (see below) oversaw the day-to-day work. Indeed, by May 1763, Freebairn was also involved with mines on Islay, Tillicoultry, other mines in the Ochils and elsewhere. By September 1764 he boasts that the Islay mines 'go better than any other in Scotland except Leadhills'. And in February 1766 Freebairn writes gloatingly from Islay ...'The furnace is going here and the barrs mounting in piles like the pyramids in the plain of Mummies' (12).

Robert Wilson seems to have been one of the partners at Tillicoultry, carried out a survey at Loss in the early 1750s and was involved again at Alva in 1758 when he was resentful of being told what to do by the supervisor there, John Williamson. He supervised the short-lived venture at Loss in 1760-1 and was one of the intermediaries introducing Patten and Richardson to the area . Freebairn was always anxious to have his view but was disparaging of his capabilities. Writing in February 1762, for example, he says

> *I have engaged Wilson to procure miners and oversee them work not according to his own opinion but expressly by mine.... He is a great fool but may be useful ... write to me what Wilson has to say'.*

He was supervisor at Logie until shortly before the work lapsed but had moved to Otterburn by May 1765 before disappearing altogether. John Williamson 'oversman at Alva' appears intermittently from 1758, working at Alva and Bridge of Allan and Logie. In 1770 he was in Islay but was also supervising at Bridge of Allan and visiting other mining operations. He is the writer of the long Report on the Mines of the Wester Airthrey Company dated 26 September 1770. In 1775 Haldane thought him too little there but that he was a man who could be confided in and who understood the mine as he had been a workman himself.

Finding labour clearly presented problems for an industry which had short and long term fluctuations. Miners were brought in as required, from Closeburn, Islay and elsewhere and were moved about between the various Ochils sites as the work fluctuated. At Alva in 1758 two teams were set up as rivals, to encourage greater effort; more often they were paid 'by bargain', that is, a team contracted to cut a specified length for an agreed fee. Wages of 1s 2d per day were being paid to the Logie miners in September 1763 but deductions for 'defective work' are recorded twice at Logie and wages were not always promptly paid. In 1762 Erskine told Nicholas Crisp that the previous year's expenses 'did not go much above two hundred pounds and we have about fourteen hands at work'. It is doubtful if any site in the Ochils exceeded (or even equalled) this figure in spite of the claim that up to 50 men had worked at Tillicoultry. At Logie the maximum was six; some worked only for a short period and no miner seems to have worked through the entire period of operation at Logie. James Gilchrist was injured at work at harvest time 1763, his injuries were treated but he did not return to the payroll. The miners were recognised to be skilled employees and when Mr Philips came from Cornwall to inspect the old workings it was a former miner who showed him around. John Williamson, overseer, had evidently been a miner himself so there was a degree of social mobility.

The most interesting of the English investors were Patten and Richardson, two men from Cheshire. They were involved with lead mines both at Tyndrum and Minigaff (13). They were briefly amongst the most enthusiastic investors in the Ochils and clearly had some technical expertise; both visited Scotland to inspect their mines. They knew John Sickler and James Stephens, who had both previously worked in the Ochils and had acted as intermediaries to introduce them to local landowners. In June 1761, Patten wrote to Wright asking about potential transport costs. He visited Loss in June 1762 and Patten and Richardson later entered into contracts for the west side of Alva, for Loss and Lipney and for part of Keir and at least negotiated for Blairlogie and other local mines in addition to involving themselves in the lead mines referred to above.

Discussion

Henry Kalmeter identified the main difficulties facing mineral mining in Scotland as widespread ignorance of the whole subject, lack of capital and governmental indifference to the economy. Supplies were readily available from Sweden, the Baltic and from England, whilst 'consumption within the country is nothing, and manufactories are unknown'. The more specific local difficulty of the inaccessibility of the Ochils mines was only partly offset by the abundance of water-power 'to drive a wheel for a smelting house' and by the availability of coal and water transport *via* the Forth. By the time of Kalmeter's visit Erskine had begun to build a smelting and refining house at Alva – which might, of course, have been used to process ore from other sites had the Alva mine itself been still working. Otherwise there is no evidence for on-site processing in the Ochils and in the 1760s. Nicholas Crisp was against processing the cobalt on site at Alva until it was certain that there was sufficient ore to justify the cost. Here was a key paradox for the Ochils mines; the potential advantage of local refining could only be justified if the supply of ore was going to be maintained. Even in 1800, ore from Bridge of Allan was carried to Alloa to be processed.

But the excitement of the early 1760s did introduce a potential local advantage, in that clusters of mines were expected to attract 'adventurers' to a neighbourhood, giving all the proprietors an interest in encouraging the local industry. Briefly, at least, Patten and Richardson were able to move miners from site to site within the area according to the promise of the veins or the exigencies of water or other problems.

The biggest ventures were the Alva Silver Mine, the Alva Cobalt Mine, the Tillicoultry Copper Mine and the Bridge of Allan episode from 1762 until the early 1770s. All involved significant finance and expertise from outside the immediate locality. Alva Cobalt Mine was a fully-fledged joint-stock company. Even the smaller ventures were never totally reliant on local finance. But total capital committed was rarely huge. Patten and Richardson could move in quickly as interest grew but could detach themselves equally quickly as prospects faded. Individual lairds spread their risks across several mines and, whilst most probably lost money, none appear to have gone in so deeply as to bankrupt themselves.

The documentation covers a wide range of issues, including transport, access, the sorting and processing of the ores and so on. But the richest haul · came from the papers of James Wright, laird of Loss between his father's death in 1745 and his own death in 1769. As part of his process of self-education, Wright contacted many people he thought could inform him about both the technical and business aspects; he added to the papers he would have inherited from his grandfather and father by borrowing papers from his neighbours, in effect creating an archive about mines and mining in eighteenth century Scotland because he recognised that informing himself about the procedure and the history of mines was likely to be a useful and profitable exercise.

He collected papers relating to Alva, Blairlogie, Logie (even prior to his own involvement there), Bridge of Allan (contemporaneously with the work there in the 1760s) Pendreich and Keir. His ability to do that is not surprising; Wright was a popular and genial man and would have known the proprietors of all these estates. Indeed, many of them were his partners and co-adventurers in the mining business; he and Lord Barjarg were partners in sheep farming, Haldane of Airthrey was his trusted friend whose land was integral to Wright's plans to transform Menstrie Glen from small farms into a sheep walk (14). When he wanted a copy of Mr Jones's contract for Blairlogie, he sent a letter to Dundas of Manor who quickly replied, enclosing the document – which Wright duly returned after copying it. At the same time, he kept a copy of his own request and of his own reply – something he only did with 'important' letters. So Wright used an extensive local network of contacts both to forge business links and to glean information.

Further afield he had documents relating to Strontian, Tyndrum and Wanlockhead. He was able to keep in touch with events at all these places and also with Freebairn in Islay. And via Sickler, he was able to locate Stephens (who had previously visited Loss) and to set up the links with Patten and Richardson in Cheshire as they tried to expand their operations to Scotland. Both of these partners visited Loss and Wright established friendly relations with them – they must have exchanged technical information. And *via* the Erskines and Haldane he had at least indirect contact with Nicholas Crisp with his wide connections and high expertise. James Fergus, Wright's cousin and legal adviser, wrote to Wright when he met a gentleman 'considerably concerned in mines', knowing that he might be a useful contact.

Perhaps the most remarkable archival find is a 'reading list' dated 1763 and in Wright's own writing (15). There is no direct information about the circumstances of the list being made but it is one of many jottings, on a wide range of topics, which survive amongst his papers. There are four 'names' on his list which is headed by Georgius Agricola, the sixteenth century writer on mines; Wright notes that he writes in Latin and is 'the best writer upon Mines'. He also notes 'Helvas, a German & a physician & a director of the Emperor of Germany's mines'. Very curiously, the next reference is to 'a Swed (sic) that writes on the Mines in Scotland. He takes notice of the Earl of Stirling's copper mines near Menstry and this place and the Lead Hills mines…'. This, surely, can only refer to Henry Kalmeter, whose account of his journey was not to be available in published form until 1978. And finally, he lists 'Mr Place an English gentleman who was concerned in Mines in Scotland and who is a very sensible, clever man …' going on to outline Place's reported views on Highland mineral veins. Place does not appear to have published anything but Abraham

Place at Strontian, agent and manager for the partners in the Clifton Mines is on record in 1734.

The links were not without problems, however. Nicholas Crisp, the most 'scientific' of those with a direct interest in the mines, wrote in September 1761, enclosing a copy of his thesis on the refining of cobalt ores, stating that he was anxious to further knowledge 'so as to steer between the common attention of miners to one ore only and the visionary pursuits of Allchymists.' But a few weeks later, more commercially, he advised that the presence of silver should not be made public if it was not already generally known. The following year, 'since the affair of Airthrey has made some talk' Haldane was approached by a David Main who assured him he knew something nobody else did about Airthrey and tried to get a half share in the mine and full control of the management. Main also spoke to Crisp. He did not know the extent of Crisp's existing involvement and told him that he was certain that there was great wealth in the hills, suggesting they might buy shares cheaply 'and get immense profit'. Crisp, whilst concealing his own prior involvement, assured him of a reward for useful information but blocked Main's further involvement. Crisp described him as speculative and ingenious but not experienced.

But these events highlight a fundamental problem for this sort of network. Who was to be trusted when all had their own interest to consult? Were the supposed experts expert? Were they honest? Men who were paid to find minerals and supervise their extraction, can hardly be blamed if they tended to see rosy prospects if just a little more work, a little more money, were expended. And men like Haldane, who had sunk considerable sums in the mines, were always sorely tempted to believe them.

At least some of the analyses of the 1760s and 1770s were being carried out in Scotland by Joseph Black though Crisp, based in London, was more important. And even Sir Isaac Newton, consulted by the government about the value of the Alva silver, had recognised that his knowledge of the pure sciences was of limited use in deciding on practical mining issues. Perhaps the new generation of prospectors in the 1760s were more skilful than those who had gone before. But nothing could get round the problem of assessing what was behind the rock face. In 1762, as the prospects at Loss began to fade, Richardson wrote to Wright that he would try to see further into the rock than Stephens. In 1761 Crisp was certain that the hills which contained silver must contain other higher metals but in the same letter recognises that a smelter should not be built until supplies were certain. Crisp wondered aloud if a German miner might be useful. They were skilful but would be expensive, he said, and their knowledge of manufacture was poor – evidently it was decided that even the cobalt did not justify the expense or the risk. William Fergusson, a merchant from Ayr, expressed similar worries. The miners of Scotland were ignorant of cobalt and the Alva venturers would need German expertise, he wrote. But a proper person would be difficult to find and expensive to retain, the Saxon proprietors would endeavour to frustrate their efforts and a bad choice could betray their trust. Mr Seyfert 'the Saxon gentleman' assured Lord

Barjarg that his own system 'cannot fail'; it was, surely, wise to ignore such approaches!

In the end, much came down to the old fashioned idea of reputation. Thomson had assured Wright in the 1730s that the potential partners were 'gentlemen of honour, honesty and probity, nowayes litigious nor inclined to law suits'. Mr Stephens assured Wright that Patten and Richardson were 'two of as worthy gentlemen as is in England. I have served Mr Patten this sixteen years or more.' Wright, meanwhile, assured Patten that Mr Sickler had a good reputation in Scotland and that Squire Shuttleworth's steward could inform Patten about Wright himself.

For the miners, it was dangerous and transient work. They appear to have been quite mobile, both locally and nationally; perhaps some were English. And the case of John Williamson suggests that there was at least a potential for social mobility. The supervisors and technical experts were very mobile. Seyfert was from Saxony and Sickler and Vangen are not likely to have been Scots. Philips came from Cornwall. And so on. They had extensive links and contacts and used them. Crisp, in particular, was in touch with other experts across Europe. Again, the Ochils mines were but an episode for most of them; when they failed to generate the expected profits they pulled out and moved their attention elsewhere. For the local lairds the situation was somewhat different. Their attention was primarily on their own land. They hoped that mines would make they rich. But they knew that rashness would make them poor. Sir Charles Erskine's reported remark that 'out of *that* hole I took fifty thousand pounds and I put it all into *that* hole', is a simplification as Erskine found a good many holes into which to pour money but, like other local lairds, he tempered his excitement with caution; they seem to have avoided heavy losses.

Bibliography

Boswell, J., 1955, *The Journal of a Tour to the Hebrides with Samuel Johnson*, (1785).

Colvin, H., 1995, *A Biographical Dictionary of British Architects 1600-1840*, Yale University Press.

Dickie D. M., Forster, C. W. (ed) 1974, *Mines and Minerals of the Ochils*, Clackmannanshire Field Studies Society.

Durie, A. J., 1993 'Bridge of Allan. 'Queen of Scottish Spas' Its nineteenth century development as a health resort', *Forth Naturalist and Historian*, Vol. 16, pp. 91-103.

Fergusson, R.M., 1905, *Logie; a Parish History*, vol II.

E. H. Francis, W. A. Read, & M. Armstrong, 1970, *The Geology of the Stirling District*, HMSO.

Jackson, B., 1994, 'Mineral Rescue Collecting at the Alva Silver Mines' *Forth Naturalist and Historian*, Vol. 17, pp. 3-4.

Thomas H McGrail, 1940, *Sir William Alexander, First Earl of Stirling, a Biographical Study*, Edinburgh.

Mitchell A., and J S Clark (ed) 1908, *MacFarlane's Geographical Collection*, Scottish History Society, vol 53.

Moir D. G., (ed) 1973, *The Early Maps of Scotland to 1850, Vol 1*, Royal Scottish Geographical Society, pp. 65-78.

Murray, A. L., 1999, 'The Scottish Mint after the recoinage, 1709-1836', *Proceedings of the Society of Antiquaries of Scotland*, Vol. 129, p. 867 and notes.

Osburn W., 1978, 'Tillicoultry' *Statistical Account of Scotland*, (1792).
Paul R., (ed) 1904, 'Letters and Documents Relating to Robert Erskine, 1677-1720', *Miscellany of the Scottish History Society*, Vol. 44, pp. 414-6.
Proctor, J., & Bacon, M.E., 1978, 'The Plants and Soils of two mineral workings in the Ochil Hills,' *Forth Naturalist and Historian*, Vol. 3, pp.71-77.
Register of the Privy Council of Scotland, Addenda 1545-1625, Vol 14, Edinburgh, 1898.
Roger, C., 1851, *A Week at Bridge of Allan*, Edinburgh, pp. 4 –14.
Royal Commission on the Ancient and Historical Monuments of Scotland, 2001, *'Well Shelterd & Watered': Menstrie Glen, a farming landscape near Stirling.*.
Smout, T. C., 1969, 'Lead-mining in Scotland 1650-1850', *Studies in Scottish Business History* (ed. P. L. Payne) London, see particularly pp. 105 & 111 for Alva.
Smout, T. C., 1978, 'Journal of Henry Kalmeter's Travels in Scotland' *Scottish Industrial History; a Miscellany*, Scottish History Society, pp.35-39.
Turnbull, J., 1997, 'Scottish Cobalt and Nicholas Crisp', *Transactions of the English Ceramic Circle*, Vol 16, pp. 144-151.
Whatley, C. A.,1987, *The Scottish Salt Industry 1570-1850; an Economic and Social History*, Aberdeen University Press.

Manuscript sources
Falkirk Council Archives (FCA) GD171 Forbes of Callendar Papers.
National Archives of Scotland (NAS) GD18/1173 Clerk of Penicuik Papers
NAS, GD198/189 and /190, Haldane of Gleneagles Papers
NAS, RH15/115, Wright of Loss Papers.
National Library of Scotland, MS 5098 and MS 5099 Paul Collection.
Glasgow City Archives (GCA) Keir and Cadder Papers T/ SK
Chester City Record Office CR 352, Letter Book of Daniel Peck, merchant, Chester, 1703-4.

Acknowledgments

I am grateful to the Society of Antiquaries of Scotland for financial support of the documentary research and to the Royal Commission on the Ancient and Historical Monuments of Scotland for permission to use some material discovered whilst engaged on research for them. My particular thanks to Jack Stevenson for support and interest. John Ballantyne kindly supplied useful references from his own researches. Lindsay Corbett supplied many references and was 'a mine of information!'. Staff at Falkirk Archives, Glasgow City Archives, the National Library of Scotland and National Archives of Scotland were (as ever) charming and efficient.

---

1 Copies have been deposited for consultation with the National Monuments Record of Scotland and with Stirling Council Archives. For a copy on disc please apply in writing to the author.

2 NLS MS5098 f. 18r-19r, Memorandum of Facts Concerning the Mines of Alva, 1753.

3 RH15/115/4/2, bundle E, 1745 tack of Dundas of Manor's Logie mines to Thomas Jones: NAS, RH15/115/1/1 bundle G, 27 Jan 1763, Agreement between John Henderson, tacksman of Logie, with special consent of Edward Main of Powis [*ie* Mayne of Powhouse] ... and James Wright of Loss, with attached Plan, showing Logie Mine.

4 NLS, MS5098, f. 129r-v, 26 Sept 1761, Nicholas Crisp to James Erskine: ibid, f. 132, 1 Nov 1761, Nicholas Crisp: ibid f. 139, 23 Nov 1761, a man has been sent from Cornwall

to Captain Haldane: NAS, RH15/115/5/2, bundle J, 12 Dec 1761, George Cockburn to James Wright re Mr Philips.

5   NAS, RH15/115/5/2 bundle J nd, note in James Wright's hand regarding visit with Philips to Airthrey mine.

6   NAS, RH15/115/1/1 bundle F, 29 July 1763, Nicholas Crisp to Lord Barjarg about Airthrey ore: NLS MS5099, f. 21r-v, Nicholas Crisp to Haldane, copied to Erskine and to James Wright of Loss: Wright's copy is NAS, RH15/115/1/1 bundle F endorsed 'part of a letter from Mr Crisp to Lord Barjarg about the Airthrey Ore', London 29 July 1763; ibid, 24 Aug 1763, Nicholas Crisp to Haldane.

7   OSA, Logie, page 561-2.

8   NAS, GD198/189 and /190 Haldane of Gleneagles Papers, 15 July 1764, charter of mines etc.

9   FCA, GD171/3771, Report of the Mines of the Wester Airthrey Company by John Williamson 26th September 1770.

10 NLS 5099 f. 148, 12 March 1779, letter from Geo Haldane, from Airthrey Mine House.

11 Colvin, 1995 'Charles Freebairn'.

12 NAS RH15/115/5/1 bundle E Charles Freebairn to James Wright 17 Feb 1766.

13 Smout, 1967, p.118 for Patten and Richardson at Tyndrum and Minigaff. NAS, GD18/1173 Clerk of Penicuik Papers, Patten and Richardson involved in lead mines in Dumfriesshire; this collection contains other relevant documents.

14 Royal Commission on the Ancient and Historical Monuments of Scotland, 2001, 26-8.

15 NAS RH15/115/11/1 bundle F, memorandum about writers on mines, 1763.

Table 1 Mine Site Names in the Ochils.

Site	Dickie & Forster 1974 name & number	Francis & Read 1970 name & OS Ref	Notes
Bridge of Allan	Airthrey Hill mine (2) and probably east bank of Allan Water (1).	Allan Water (NS787983) and Airthrey Hill Mine (NS795978).	The probable source of the 'Airthrey silver mine' story.
Logie	Airthrey Silver Mine (3).	Airthrey Silver Mine (NS81529720).	'Old' mine on record in 1715. Sketch of site in Wright of Loss papers. No evidence of silver production here.
Blairlogie	Blairlogie (4).	Blairlogie Trials; Fig 31 shows extensive trials.	Only passing references found.
Loss	Jerah (5).	Jerah Mine (NS83239949 and NS83009982).	This mine is on Loss rather than Jerah which is south and east of the Crunie Burn.
Menstrie	Balquharn Mines (7).	Balquharn Burn Trials, various sites noted around NS86539782.	Probable site of Earl of Stirling's mines of c. 1607 also worked in mid 18th century.
Carnaughton	Carnaughton (8).	Carnaughton Glen Silver Mine (NS87819754).	'airshaft' in 1762; said to be barren in 1771.
Alva	Alva Silver Mines (9).	Alva Silver Mine, Fig 32 shows the extensive workings.	Many sites indentifiable from Alva papers.
Tillicoultry	Sites 10 and 11 cannot be distinguished in the sources.	Tillicoultry (NS91249780) Kirk (NS92349812) & Daiglen Burns (NS91069834).	Only passing references found.
Dollar	Dollar (12)	Dollar Burn (NN94550021).	Only one passing reference found.
Pendreich		Pendreich (NS80659922).	Only passing references found.
Keir/Wood of Keir might include Knockhill		Western bank of Allan Water (NS787983).	Records cannot distinguish these sites.

THE FOUNDING OF GARTMORE IN 1725

G.A. Dixon

The Scotland we know can be described as one of the most urbanised nations in Europe, with 93.1 % of its inhabitants living in cities, towns and villages having at least three-figure populations at the time of the last census before the country's long established administrative boundaries were swept away in 1975 (1). Three centuries ago, it was one of the least urbanised (2). The lack of quantified demographic information for the early years of the 18th century renders precise comparisons impossible, but such evidence as does survive indicates that most Scots – one might even, remembering how family historians normally find their forebears of that time living on farms, claim that almost all Scots – were then living rurally, at one or other of the various levels of farming society. The change from one state to the other was revolutionary.

The exceptionally rapid urbanisation of Georgian Scotland has been discussed by historians more in relation to the expansion of existing cities and other burghs (3) than as a remarkable efflorescence of new settlement centres on "greenfield" (or perhaps more often rough-pasture) and heather-moor sites. The 500 or so new settlements planned in Scotland during the four thirds of a century before 1854 (4), although they have not been neglected by historical geographers (5), have received scant attention from most historians of the period. The standard historical paper remains Smout's, *The Landowner and the Planned Village in Scotland, 1730-1830*, first published in 1970 (6), which listed 126 new towns and villages and by its choice of 1730 as a starting date has left the impression that the 1730s were the launching decade for the planned settlement movement north of the Border.

With some 22 planned settlements originating between the 1670s and the 1700s, the current Stirling administrative area has almost a quarter of them – Buchlyvie, 1672; Thornhill, 1696; Gargunnock, 1721; Gartmore, 1725, and Buchany, 1728 – with foundation dates in the 60 years immediately preceding 1730 (7). All five were feued off along existing, or slightly realigned, traffic routes, but one of them, Gartmore, has novel features which make it of particular interest.

The Gartmore estate had been bought by Sir William Graham son of John Graham of Duchray in 1644, and on his only son Sir John Graharm's death unmarried in 1708, the estate passed to the latter's young niece Mary, whose rapid disposal of the Gartmore lands to her brother-in-law Robert Graham, left successive generations of her own descendants disputing the transfer until they too died out in the 19th century (8). In November 1723, Robert Graham entailed the Gartmore estate on his eldest son Nicol Graham an advocate, and his heirs, specifically granting him and them the right to feu any part of the barony, apart from the mansion house and its policies, in order to form a new town upon it. Three months later, Nicol Graham received a crown charter of the estate and was infeft upon it in March 1724 (and again, an error in the notarial docquet having been noticed, in September 1755) (9).

As Nicol Graham Younger of Gartmore (10), the young advocate proceeded to choose a site for his new town on undulating ground with a slight summit just east of the existing road between the parish kirks of Aberfoyle and Drymen and just north of the Perthshire-Stirlingshire boundary. Such preliminary work as realigning the highway to form a spinal street, setting down march stones and drafting the provisions of a standard feu charter was carried out, but there is no indication that a numbered feuing plan of the new settlement was prepared: those were still pioneering times (11). The first two feu charters were granted on 20th August 1725 to John Mcaie (*i.e.*, Mackay), maltman, and John Taylor, whose chosen building plots lay side by side on the north side of the street (12). Each occupied a rood of ground (a quarter of a Scots acre) and had a street frontage of 60 feet. Taylor's annual feu duty, the payment of which was to commence at Whitsunday 1726, was set at £3 Scots and Mcaie's at 30 shillings Scots, but the latter was also, by his charter, granted two acres of land in feu beyond the rectangle assigned to contain the new village's building plots and immediately behind the initial pair of plots. The feu duty for the two acres of what was in effect to be croft land was set at £7 Scots per acre, with the initial payment again due at Whitsun 1726. Both settlers were permitted to quarry stone and cut turf for building purposes at sites appointed by the founder, and to cast peats in the peat moss to be used by the villagers.

If one compares the layout plans of Gartmore and Thornhill (13), its late-17th-century predecessor, three points immediately leap to the eye. Gartmore has at its centre a square or market place; Thornhill has not. Thornhill, however, has a North and a South Common just beyond its building plots; Gartmore has neither. And Gartmore's longitudinal plot boundaries run at right angles from the street and are of lengths consistent with an overall rectangular "envelope" for the village, whereas Thornhill's plot boundaries are much less regular both in length and in rectangularity. Gartmore, the later, Georgian, member of the pair, is, in a word, more symmetrical.

Thornhill's founder, Archibald Napier of Boquhapple, had been given the right to hold four annual fairs and a weekly market only seven months before he granted the first feu charters of his new village, and the commons there comfortably accommodated them (14). Fourteen years previously, the Scottish Parliament had granted Sir William Graham very similar rights: "*Considering That the town [i.e., fermtoun called the Midlethrid of Gartmore ... Is a place very convenient for keeping of yearlie ffaires and a weekly mercat to the advantage of His Ma[jes]ties subjects*", rights were granted to hold "*ffour free ffaires [there] ... The first upon the fifth day of May to be called Beltane ffair The second upon the Sexteenth day of July to be Called St Marks ffair The thrid upon the Eight day of October to be called Gartmore fair And the fourth upon the Tuenty eight day of december To be called St Johns fair yearlie with libertie also of a weekly mercat to be keeped ... upon wednesday weekly in all time comeing*"(15).

To accommodate those economic and social gatherings, Nicol Graham had a single, central market place laid out in his new village. Only 40 yards across, it was appreciably smaller than many market squares in later Scottish planned settlements, but it was a Georgian beginning (16). Centralising Gartmore's fairs and markets removed the need for commons at the outer ends of the building plots, thus enabling the founder to make available individual holdings of acres of arable land close to the planned rectangle. John Mcaie's two acres at Gartmore pioneered the encircling of many later settlements by 'Lotted Lands' but with one significant dissimilarity. As Lockhart has recently summarised: Between 1720 and the 1850s some 490 planned villages, characterised by a regular layout of streets, building plots and adjacent fields (or Lotted Lands) were founded on estates throughout Scotland ... Lotted lands were fields, typically subdivided into one- or two-acre lots, which were leased to villagers to grow crops such as oats and turnips and for grazing cattle and horses. Agricultural activities were particularly important where labouring and domestic industries provided insufficient employment (17). By leasing, rather than feuing, those encircling lots, often annually, later town and village founders retained a powerful means of social control over a population of otherwise independent feuars or holders of long building leases (which could run for centuries). If a 'tenementer' misbehaved, the lease of his lotted land need not be renewed. By feuing, rather than leasing, the acres immediately around his new settlement, Nicol Graham deprived himself, at least to the extent of those feus, of this means of disciplining its inhabitants.

During its early decades Gartmore's street of building plots gradually filled out, as new feuars settled, and the feuable neighbouring acres were taken up. In 1729, George Simme, merchant, feued a building rood on the south side of the street, and two arable acres (18), while James Graham feued on the same side only a building rood (19) and Williain McCoserich, shoemaker, only two acres of arable (20). William Wood, tailor (21) and John Ferguson (22) feued smaller plots in 1730, while in the same year a professional element appeared in the person of Eneas Mcqueen, surgeon, feuing two neighbouring half roods (23). Further settlers followed, though not every year. By 1734 a half feu fronting the cross-containing market place was being taken by a vintner, John Murray (24), and a minister of the gospel, Mr John Connacher, took over an existing half feu from James Bain, gardener (25). The list of feuars lengthened as the middle of the century approached, and by 1753 Nicol Graham had switched to 500-year building leases, which cost the settlers less in legal fees and for most practical purposes were virtually equivalent to feus (26).

The founder of Gartmore died on 16th November 1775, a full half century after granting his first building plots within its neat rectangle (27). He was succeeded by his second, and eldest surviving, son, Robert Graham, who had already inherited the Ardoch estate from his cousin, William Bontine, and who was, by inheriting in 1796 the estate of Finlayston from the last Earl of Glencairn, to bring into the family the additional surname Cunninghame, all three surnames being drawn to the notice of a wider world by his great-great-grandson, the South American adventurer, Robert Bontine Cunninghame Graham, (1852-1936), who had to sell the Gartmore estate in 1900 (28). Within months of the founder's death, Robert Graham employed James Richmond to survey the barony of Gartmore and the resulting plan includes the oldest surviving cartographic depiction of the village in any detail (29). It does not show the cross standing in the middle of the Square, as Charles Ross's plan was to do in 1781 (30), and William McKinlay's in 1792 (31), but it does display a village most of whose building plots had already been taken up (32). Unlike that other Graham foundation some six miles to the north-east of Gartmore, the now-vanished village of New Grahamstown (33), Nicol Graham's pioneering manifestation of Georgian town planning still flourishes, compactly, as it approaches its tercentenary.

References and notes

1. General Register Office: *Index of Scottish Place Names from 1971 Census, with location and Population (over 100 persons)*, 1975, Appendixes 4 and 7.
2. Whyte, I.D.: Urbanization in Eighteenth-Century Scotland pp. 176-194. In Devine T.M. and Young, JR., eds.: *Eighteenth Century Scotland: New Perspectives*, 1999.
3. Allan, D.: *Scotland in the Eighteenth Century: Union and Enlightenment*, 2002, p. 83; Whyte, I.D.: Scottish and Irish urbanisation in the seventeenth and eighteenth centuries: a comparative perspective, pp. 14-28. In Connolly, S.J., Houston, R.A. and Morris, R.J., eds.: *Conflict, Identity and Economic Development: Ireland and Scotland, 1600-1939*, 1995.
4. Lockhart, D. G.: Lotted lands and planned villages in north-east Scotland, pp. 17-40. In *The Agricultural History Review*, vol.49, pt. 1 (2001); Lockhart, D. G.: Planned Settlements in Georgian Scotland: Aims and Outcomes, lecture delivered at the Association of Heritage Societies in Mid-Scotland's conference on 17th May 2003 on *Scotland's Forgotten Revolution: Three Centuries of our New Towns, New Villages and New Suburbs*.
5. Lockhart, D.G.: The planned villages, pp. 249-270. In Parry, M.L. and Slater, T.R., eds.: *The Making of the Scottish Countryside*, 1980.
6. Smout, T.C.: The Landowner and the Planned Village in Scotland, 1730-1830, pp. 73-106. In Phillipson, N.T. and Mitchison, R., eds.: *Scotland in the Age of Improvement: Essays in Scottish History in the Eighteenth Century*, 1970.
7. Dixon, G.A.: Planned Towns and Villages in the Stirling Area, 1670s-1900s. In *Focus*, (forthcoming).
8. Pirie-Gordon, H., ed.: *Burke's Genealogical and Heraldic History of the Landed Gentry*, 1937, p. 946; National Archives of Scotland: Cunninghame Graham Papers: GD22/4/63/6: John Bogle, senior, to John Bogle, junior, 22nd November 1778.
9. GD22/3/503/31: Memorial for W.C.C. Graham of Gartmore about the succession to the estate of Gartmore, 1826.
10. Robert Graham of Gartmore died in 1730: GD22/1/459/6 and 7.
11. GD22/1/459/1: feu disposition to John Mcaie, 1725.
12. GD22/1/459/1 and 2.
13. Dixon, G.A.: The Founding of Thornhill in 1696 pp. 75-82. In the *Forth Naturalist and Historian*, vol. 18 (1995)
14. *Ibid.*, p.76.
15. Thomson, T., ed.: *The Acts of the Parliaments of Scotland*, vol.VIII, 1820, p.441.
16. Ordnance Survey, 1:2500, Perthshire, sheet CXXX.9 (surveyed 1864). Gartmore Square was not, however, the first such square proposed in Scotland – see Bardgett. F.D.: *Scotland Reformed: The Reformation in Angus and the Mearns*, 1989, p. 152, which reproduces a redrawn version of the 'Pourtraicte of the new citie of Edzel, 4 Septeb. 1592: idea' now in the John Rylands Library in Manchester.

17. See 4, 200 1, p. 17.
18. GD22/1/459/4.
19. GD22/1/459/5.
20. GD22/1/459/3.
21. GD22/1/459/6.
22. GD22/1/459/7.
23. GD22/1/459/8.
24. GD22/1/459/11.
25. GD22/459/10.
26. GD22/1/508/53.
27. Stirling Council Archives: Cook Papers: PD16/7: Rob. Stewart to Wm. McKillop, 19th December 1775.
28. See 8, 1937, pp. 946-947.
29. National Library of Scotland: Map Library: Acc.4325(2): Plan of the Barrony of Gartmore ... Surveyed and Deliniated by James Richmond 1776.
30. NLS: Acc. 1133 5/185: A Plan of the Town of Gartmore, by Charles Ross, 1781.
31. *Ibid.*: Gartmore Town, by William McKinlay, November 1792.
32. Richmond's plan shows, however, several vacant plots on both sides of the street in the vicinity of the present church, not then built, and two smaller gaps at or near the extremities of the northern side of the street.
33. SCA: MP/PC/1: James Stobie's map of Perthshire, 1783.

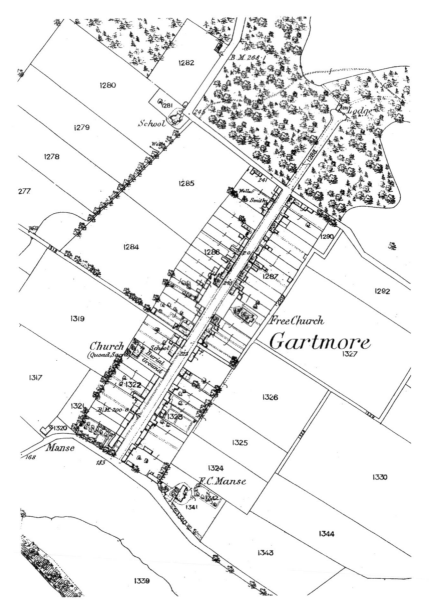

OS 1:2500 survey of Gartmore (1864).
(Reproduced by permission of the Trustees, National Library of Scotland.)

ANNIE STEEDMAN HUNTER: A VERY RADICAL REFORMER
People of the Forth (14)

A.J. and C.E. Durie

In Logie graveyard is to be found, to the east of the church, a plain memorial obelisk, which marks the burying place of the Hunter family, some of whom are buried in the lair. On it are inscribed the family names, headed up by Archibald Hunter, the Glasgow upholsterer turned hydropathist who had moved with his family to Bridge of Allan from Gilmorehill in 1865 and had been in charge of the Ochilview Hydro until his death in 1894. His first wife, who died in May 1875 is listed there; as are two of the daughters, Mary (d. 1882) and Agnes (d. 1871); as are the sons William (d. 1894, and buried at Matlock); and Dr Charles Dearie Hunter who died of TB in California in 1883.

There is, however, one notable exception amongst the names listed, whom one might have expected to find. It is that of Annie Steedman Hunter, William Hunter's second wife, who died in April 1914 and of whom there is no mention. She is not in view, nor is her memory much in anybody's mind nowadays. But in her time, at and around the turn of the nineteenth century, she was a figure of some importance, a woman of many causes, a prolific writer of articles and pamphlets, a practitioner of alternative or complementary medicine with a substantial practice, an advocate of vegetarianism, a Christian Spiritualist, and supporter of cremation. In an age where activism was a way of life for some, she was exceptional; although perhaps not quite on a par with the radical Professor Newman who described himself as "Anti-slavery, anti-alcohol, anti-tobacco, anti-*everything*" (1). But she shared many causes with him and his like – and indeed it is quite likely that they knew each other – through such causes as opposition to vaccination and vivisection. One cause, though she endorsed it, which received relatively little attention from her was temperance, although alcohol was certainly on her prescribed list, and tobacco equally anathema.

She had a very active life, and well deserves recognition as a health reformer, albeit at the fringe. Her most significant cause, which she combined with an active continuance of her husband's hydropathic practice, was vegetarianism, but she also combined this with a range of other radical causes, including (according to family memory) spiritualism (2).

Spiritualists regarded monopolies like the medical profession with deep suspicion, supported a change in the law relating to women's rights, and contributed to the causes of abolition and prison and lunacy reform. A preoccupation with topics like vegetarianism, homeopathy, natural healing and temperance reflected a concern with the purification of the mind in preparation for heightened spirituality as well as a desire for personal control over health and well being (3).

She seems to have been at her most active around the turn of the nineteenth century, *i.e.* after her husband's death in 1894: in practice as a healer, as a writer of pamphlets, articles and letters to the Scottish press and in specialist magazines, and as a speaker. She was a formidable woman, which is very much the impression given by her photograph (although Victorian portraits seldom conveyed anything than severity), and rather feared by the family into which she had married. Dora Kirkwood, whose mother was a step daughter of the second Mrs Hunter, recalled that "She was a vegetarian, a spiritualist, also I believe, an epileptic" (4). Not surprisingly she was always known by her as Mrs Hunter, though the girls who were still at home with their father at Bridge of Allan were allowed to call her 'Agnes'. Dora's grandfather, who had died when she was only five, she remembered with affection as possessed of a quiet magnetic charm, but not so Annie Steedman. "She used to appear unannounced to pay us a visit, and we had to go and see her at Bridge of Allan, but we could never love her. She had a bee in her bonnet, not only vegetarian but spiritualistic, and used to tell us she had been communicating with my grandfather long after he was dead." She inspired respect amongst those who met her: Metcalfe, the veteran hydropathist and historian of the hydropathic movement, who knew her well, said of her

> "Her pen was never weary; her voice seldom at rest when the opportunity presents itself for advancing the cause of hygienic reform. Her parable is chiefly upon diet and against the eating of flesh food. In short Mrs Hunter has accepted the vegetarian principles and sees in them the one hope for the renovation and regeneration of the human race. This is her pet theory and other measures, in comparison, are regarded as of secondary importance, including hydropathy, in which her late husband did so good a work' (5).

Mrs Hunter, therefore, is a figure who should not be left unrecognised. This paper will review from an historian's perspective what we know of her life, and then offer an assessment from the viewpoint of a literary specialist of some of her writing, in the hope of bringing her name forward for fuller study. There has been no biography, nor were her obituary notices other than very brief and tucked away in minor publications. 'Mrs Hunter has passed away', was all the comment that the *Vegetarian* offered in May 1914. There are no private papers of her surviving and the main sources to be examined are her writings, scattered as they are, in a range of literature from the 1890s to c. 1907.

Of her early life, we know very little, and nothing of her education or upbringing. She came from a large and wealthy Edinburgh family, her father, John Anderson, (who had been born in Stirling) being a fishmonger with premises in the heart of New Town at 106 George Street, and a substantial house at Denham Green, Trinity. The Andersons were a large family, there being one son (Peter) and six daughters (6), of which Annie was the oldest, and the first to be married, and that at the age of 37! She was Archibald Hunter's second wife, his first aged sixty having died on 31st May 1878 at Bridge of Allan. Annie Steedman was much younger than him, Archibald being 67. The

Bridge of Allan Reporter on July 3rd 1880 reported the marriage of Archibald Hunter MD Bridge of Allan to Annie Steedman Anderson at Denham Green Edinburgh on the 24th ult., by the Rev Andrew Thomson, D.D., Broughton Place UP Church, assisted by the Rev John Reid, Bridge of Allan. It may be significant that both families (Hunter and Anderson) were United Presbyterian, a denomination in Scotland which was very supportive of hydropathy. How they met is not known, but her father, a wealthy man, (7) was certainly interested in hydropathy, evidence of which is his taking 20 shares in 1874 in the newly promoted Atholl Hydropathic Company a venture at Pitlochry which turned out very poorly. It is certainly possible that the family had stayed at Hunter's hydro in Bridge of Allan, in which James Anderson was to invest after her marriage. They honeymooned at Innellan, a time somewhat disrupted by his need to return to Bridge of Allan to see how his daughters from his first marriage were getting on. Annie Steedman was to be a stepmother, but not a mother herself.

She herself lived at Zetland House, Hunter's residence across the road from the Hydro, a residence which she continued to occupy after his death in 1894. Hydropathists' wives were usually working partners in the business, looking after the management of the catering and cleaning, with some actually practising amongst the female clientele. Mrs Hunter started this at the Hydro while her husband was alive, and continued at Zetland House after his death. Her passion was diet, and in particular vegetarianism, which she urged on all, and indeed enforced on her husband who latterly was allowed only the occasional relaxation of a piece of fish (8). This was an emphasis which was shared by many hydropathists who saw a diet without meat as a key element in their therapeutic regime (9). Fruit and health foods were promoted by them, and it is no accident that the most successful of all hydrotherapists, the American Dr John Harvey Kellogg of the Battle Creek Sanatorium invented both cornflakes and peanut butter (10).

It is a reasonable inference that she was quite successful: she received many enquiries by mail, saw patients herself, who were presumably charged a consultation fee, and may indeed have had a few to stay with her. She also held a surgery at the Religious Instruction Rooms in Glasgow on Tuesdays, as well as the consultations at Zetland House on Thursdays (11). The enumerator's returns for the 1901 census taken early in April show her living at Zetland House, "on own means" with a general domestic servant Margaret Small. There were two visitors staying: a Walter R. Hudrew, physician and surgeon, aged 45 and Marie Bates, aged 32, a Salvation Army officer. Whether the latter was a friend or a patient, we do not know. In a letter to Richard Metcalfe, which he published in 1912 she claimed that she "had patients of all ranks in society, all over the country and very many from overseas...Besides two and three thousand letters per year, besides my press correspondence, and not a few visitors from our busy centres ... [there is] little margin for private claims" (12).

At the turn of the century Bridge of Allan seems to have been quite a centre of alternative medicine. At nearby Staffa Lodge, or so the 1901 census returns show, there lived a James Ramsay *Hygienic Physician Unregistered.* and his family, with some visitors, who may well have been patients. There had been resident there c. 1896, as an advertisement in the third edition of *Hunter's Hygienic Treatment*, a Hardy Moffat, who ran a Hygienic Home of the improvement and Restoration of Health by Natural Means. "Offering Fresh Air, Pure (vegetarian) Diet and Outdoor Recreations, combined with Hydropathic, Massage, or Swedish Medical Movement treatment if required".

Annie Steedman Hunter's activities reached beyond Bridge of Allan and covered a range of causes. What helped her and her activities was financial security: Zetland House was hers, and there was her income from fees and consultations, plus the dividends from her shareholdings in the Bridge of Allan Hydro which was up to 45 by May 1887. Her father John Anderson also took 10 shares in May 1882 and held these for another year, later increasing his holding to 20. Just before his death his shares were transferred in April 1890 to 'Annie' and after the share capital increase of that year she held 98 shares. She was, however, never a Director, which suggests that she chose not to take an active part in running the company. Share dividends ran at between 10 % in 1890; 6 % from 1894-1896 and 8½ % in 1900 (13). In 1890 her income would have been £98, and she acquired more shares by Archibald's death, which would have given her from that source alone a comfortable income. The Hydro did eventually lose its profitability in the last few years of her life, but perhaps by then (as we shall see) her activities and outgoings were much reduced.

Archibald Hunter was a successful hydropathist, and the Bridge of Allan Hydro a sound business which experienced none of the financial crises which were common in this sector and which were particularly severe in the early 1880s. He also had a considerable reputation as a writer, and his *Hydropathy for Home Use*, first published in 1880 was to go through many editions. Significantly, the second Mrs Hunter was to take an increasing hand in these publications, supplying, for example, a chapter on 'dietary reform' and a week's menu of vegetarian dishes with recipes to Health, Happiness and Longevity, How Obtained, embracing strictures on diet and habits (1885). Her writing was to flower in the 1890s, as did her career as a speaker. At a Hydropathic Congress or conference held in Gloucester in the autumn of 1895, she was a key speaker. It was reported that Mrs Hunter of Zetland House Hydropathic establishment gave her experiences of hydropathic treatment, and a number of varied cases showing its value in all diseases (14). In the same journal, she is reported as having written in February 1893 to the *North British Daily Mail* on practical measures for the treatment of scarlet fever.

Her writing career reached a pitch of intensity in the first years of the twentieth century. She wrote letters to the press as, for example, a letter on January 25th 1905 to the *Glasgow Evening Times* in reference to infant mortality, and another, on soap in the *Glasgow Herald*, in December 1903. Her other writings include a pamphlet *Our Young Men* in 1905 which was published by the Progressive Press, Paisley 3d, and there were a number of articles. *The Scottish Health Reformer, (and Advocate of Rational Living)*, which was published in Paisley, was virtually her house magazine for some years; and in almost every issue in the years from December 1903 until 1905 onwards she makes an appearance. Amongst the more substantial contributions were articles on *Oatmeal, Diet and Disease, With my Patients, Revaccination, Consumptive Sanatoria, A Health Talk, Juvenile Smoking* and in June 1905 *A Canker in the National Life* which is an examination of current sexual issues including contraception: her main plea is for abstinence. She writes as one of the women who have failed to carry out the command "to increase and to multiply the race of mankind". The last contribution in this journal is on *Early Marriages and Infant Mortality in our Large Cities*, in September 1905. Another favoured outlet was *The Pyscho-Therapeutic Journal*, issued by a society established in April 1901 for the Study, Investigation and Practice of Medical Hypnotism, Suggestive Therapeutics, Curative Human Radiations and Drugless Healing. Mrs Hunter subscribed to the society and sent several contributions to its journal. There was a letter to the editor in August 1905 on the *Influence of Flowers on Health* and in another article published in May 1906, pp. 47-48; *Osteopathy* she leaves clues which suggest that she was far from being as enthusiast about women's rights. "The danger of the present century will be of an emasculated manhood and a virile womanhood. Men are debasing their nervous energies by various self-indulgences and vicious habits, while women are increasing both in physical and mental strength and courage. Are we to have a new race of Amazons in whom the sexes will be reversed and the feminine take the lead?" A third location for her writing was *The Nature Cure Annual* 1907-1908, which was edited by Watson MacGregor Reid, and devoted to the Advocacy of Hydropathy, health reform, Open Air Life and Simplicitarianism. It has a photograph of her and an article called *The Heart of the Home*, pp 71-78. This appears to have been her last published piece of work.

A cause which particularly occupied her attention was that of anti-vaccination, the compulsory vaccination of children against smallpox. She threw herself into this, a controversial topic much in debate in the early twentieth century. She seems to have been particularly active in Ireland , but not in Stirling where other names feature. Her work was recognised . *The Herb Doctor* (15) in May 1914 gave her this tribute.

> "Mrs Hunter was an ardent Medical Libertarian and health reformer and worked hard for the repeal of the Compulsory Vaccination Acts. She founded the 'League of Health Defence' in 1907, which movement was backed by an editorial in our November issue of that year; but she did not get the support that her efforts deserved, the reason being that she was before her times... Mrs Hunter was a noble woman, an indefatigable worker, and a pioneer of rare foresight, as witness the anti-vaccination work in Ireland in which she took the foremost place."

She claimed some success in the letter cited above to Richard Metcalfe, which was written c. 1910 ... "We have riddled the vaccination ship in

Scotland, and we have done the same in Ireland (two thousand defaulters in Belfast today; we mean to have twenty thousand before long). Our standard is sanitation within and without, and no quarter to drug and serum treatments of any sort."

Mrs Hunter as a Writer

Mrs Hunter's publications are prolific; all bear the hallmarks of a pungent and vigorous personality. She is never less than lively and opinionated, and is a determined and energetic polemicist. Her views seem to readers a century later to be a mixture of crackpot, even dangerous, doctrine, and enlightened, robust, practical wisdom. Some are prescient and many of the issues she raises have parallels and echoes today, whilst other of her attitudes are embedded in their time. Her style is entirely consistent with her approach, heavily anecdotal rather than evidence-based (though fond of citing the odd lone medical voice, of whose report she approves), and saturated with the testimonies of those whose lives have been improved and inspired by her teachings. It incorporates religious language and authority when it suits her but in a manner that steers away from any denominational allegiance; indeed in one article she appeals to have an issue treated alike on a moral basis by Christian, Muslim and Buddhist. She is eager to employ foreign tags, italics and capitalization, so there is a sense of an emphatic speaking voice throughout, and is easy to read, accessible, lively and engaging. She is not a sitter on the fence and she does not mince her words. This is a gifted communicator in her chosen medium of magazine journalism and pamphleteering.

An overview of her creed can be swiftly provided. She is for oatmeal, commonsense, self-denial, fresh air and health education. She is against tea, intoxicants, tobacco, excessive soap (which strips the skin's natural oils), and the medicalisation of illness and disease for which there are natural remedies. Most sickness can be treated by purer lifestyle. Diet is one of her particular interests; as a convinced vegetarian, she promotes the meatless life, but her worries are at least partially about contamination in the food chain. Her mission, pursued with characteristic zeal, is to persuade the working classes of the benefits of a vegetarian diet; this group she regards as more responsive because they are unafraid of hard work and ambitious to rise socially. She is attracted to living simply and frugally, and offers as a role model a millionaire who lives on 5d a day. He is then capped by a woman who learns to live on 2d a day, half of it spent on cream; a balanced diet does not appear to function largely in these stories. Diet should be restricted in quantity – use smaller spoons, the reader is told – as well as kinds of food. One should take no liquid with food as this interferes with digestion and promotes unnatural thirst, but should chew long and thoroughly – she quotes a doctor who chews each mouthful thirty five times. Occasional fasting is a blessing, and she commends her own practice of having only one course at the main meal of the day. Hers was lunch and for three months daily she ate a rice pudding, with just a little sugar and cream. She inveighs against tea with almost as much horror as intoxicants – indeed, somewhat surprisingly she praises German beer because it is produced cheaply from pure ingredients for the Berlin working man; but she has not a good word to say about tobacco. When offered the chance to call on Thomas Carlyle, she declined, despite her admiration for his writing, because she could not bear his pipe-smoking; as both were famed for their trenchant but dissimilar views, rarely opposed by those around them, one can only speculate on the outcome of such a meeting.

If she had a particular bee in her capacious bonnet, it was that of 'No More Vaccination'. Her pamphlet of that name illustrates her distrust of both medical and legal professions, and her fear that principles are over-ridden by the desire for fees. She makes a libertarian claim of a parent's right of conscience in relation to a child's body, in the context where vaccination was compulsory for infants and non-compliance punishable with a prison sentence. Her central argument is concerned with vaccination as the violation of Nature's laws and processes. First it introduces disease to a healthy child; second, the elimination of smallpox removes from the system that which acts as a spring-cleaning agent protecting against plague (she is keen on evidence from India), fever and infant mortality. Better a small loss of beauty and the healthy defences of nature itself. Then the stories are produced which portray the dire consequences of inoculation, from syphilis (which incidentally she claims is only cured by a good dose of smallpox), erysipalas, blindness, deafness, paralysis and death. Even if there are no such consequences, it is still "a desecration of the temple of life.". In her defence it is worth noting that she makes several sound points here. Her interest is fundamentally in the immune system, in how the body defends itself, and she sees the danger of tinkering with this. Her account recognises fully the importance of social conditions in creating or preventing disease, and her remedies of "Pure air, fresh clean water and simple well-chewed food … Decent housing, good drains", for all are indeed prerequisites of health. She never claims that vegetarianism and hydropathy can protect as such, but says that the purer, healthier, happier life is less disease prone. As general statements rather than as guarantees against infectious diseases, there is little here that the twenty-first century would not endorse.

It is also worth considering Mrs Hunter's distinctive contribution writing as a woman on women, sexual health and reproduction, though some of the ambiguities and tensions visible in these areas suggest how difficult it is to apply the label of feminist to someone of her time. In the Heart of the Home (*The Nature Cure Annual* 1907-8) she argues that the first essential of a woman's married life is health of body and mind, and the prerequisite for these is the dispelling of sexual ignorance in young women; if the mother has not the gift of transmitting information, then a sympathetic woman-lecturer who has preferably been both wife and mother would be ideal. Misery and depression are all too often the result of ignorance. After this, education should cover instruction in diet and managing the family economy. Mrs Hunter knows what power issues this might raise, and states firmly a woman's freedom and right to think and decide for herself because she is the more responsible of the two. One might infer from this and other comments that the writer does not have a high view of men (teetotal, vegetarian, chaste workingmen apart), mostly it seems because she regards masculinity en masse as conspicuously lacking in self-control. However, it is noticeable that her frankness and straightforward-ness lead her to address subjects not always openly discussed. A sympathetic reviewer praises her pamphlet, *Our Young Men* against masturbation for its "daring and convincing manner". Contraception also falls within her sphere; in *A Canker in the Natural Life* she attacks contraceptives as merely abetting man's "selfishness, ignorance and pigheaded lack of control". But she fully recognised the dangers of repeated childbirth and the difficulties of large families; she rails against a 'saintly scholar' whose unfortunate wife gave birth to eight children in seven years. She is also aware that women can be abused within marriage, not least sexually, and establishes a woman's right to refuse, to receive or to share sex as she chooses. This she does with a defiant flourish of her own experience as a woman who has "failed to carry out the command to increase"; it is not clear whether her childlessness was involuntary or the result of the right to refuse. Too much sex, she says crisply, is not merely bad for the participants but also for the ensuing children who are prone to excess, lust and masturbation. Therefore voluntary abstinence is warmly recommended as the way to married happiness and the safe limitation of family size; she concludes her panegyric on this, rather splendidly, by quoting *Rule Britannia* to assert the kind of sensual slavery to which Britons should never be subjected.

Conclusion

Mrs Hunter seems to have ceased her activities abruptly in 1907, because so far nothing has been found or any writing or speaking after that date, apart from the one letter to Richard Metcalfe. It may be that the reason was ill-health; in her article entitled 'Osteopathy' which was published in 1906 she spoke of being sent to a home the previous August to have a tumour removed from her bowel and certainly her flow of writing seems to have dried up. Her eventual death, after what was described as a long illness excited no interest in the local press beyond the formal notice, (16) though given some attention in the specialist press. When her death came, the official cause on the death certificate was given as 'senile decay' (17).

There was to be no burial in Logie, where many of the Hunters, including her husband, were buried. The explanation is that cremation was another of her causes, and she was cremated at Maryhill Crematorium on the 28th April, Wylie & Lochhead having handled the arrangements, and her ashes were uplifted on May the 7th (18). She was a shareholder in the Scottish Burial Reform and Cremation Society which was registered as a limited company in December 1890, and the Western Crematorium (at Maryhill) was completed in 1895. It was not a paying investment for her; the ten £1 shares which she had purchased in December 1895 were each valued on her death at nil and 100 £1 ordinary shares in the London Cremation Company valued only at par. She did, however, leave a tidy sum, of £3,773 15s 1d (19). Her name was not added to the Hunter memorial in Logie churchyard but a plaque at the foot of the Hunter obelisk records that Vera Mary, infant daughter of Robert Hunter,

Archibald's Hunter's first son by his first marriage, an explosives merchant in Glasgow, was cremated at Maryhill· on the 29th April 1897 so perhaps her views on this topic at least had met with a favourable response from one of her stepchildren. She had plenty of opinions from which they could select.

References

1 Cited by R.B. Walker, Medical aspects of tobacco smoking and the anti-smoking movement in the Nineteenth century, *Medical History*, 1980, 24, p.399.

2 See in this context Janet Oppenheimer, *The Other World. Spiritualism and Psychical Research in England*, 1850-1914 (Cambridge 1985) which draws attention to the role of Annie Besant and the career of Dr Anna Kingsford, physician, vegetarian, vehement antis-vivisectionist and feminist who was president of the London branch of the Theosophical Society. Also Geoffrey K. Neilson, *Spiritualism and Society*, (London 1969).

3 Alex Owen, Women and nineteenth century spiritualism. Strategies in the subversion of femininity. *Disciplines of Faith*. (New York, 1987), pp 131-2.

4 Family letter from Dora Kirkwood, 16 March 1958; in the possession of Prof R.I. McCallum.

5 Richard Metcalfe, *The Rise and Progress of Hydropathy in England and Scotland*, (London 1912) p.172.

6 According to the *Census* 1881 Edinburgh North Leith 692/20 Staying at Denham Green, Trinity Road were John Anderson and his wife, a son (Peter) and five unmarried daughters, ranging in age from 29 to 18 years old.

7 He died on the 5th May 1892 and left an estate valued at £57,720 4s 6d which was divided amongst his three unmarried daughters, Victoria Magdalene Anderson, Alicia Ann Scott Anderson, and Annie Falshaw Anderson.

8 See Mrs Hunter's preface to the fourteenth edition of Hunter's *Hydropathy for Home Use* (Glasgow c 1900), he gradually left off the use of flesh foods after 1880, and except for a morsel of fish he was chiefly dependent on fruit, vegetables and whole wheaten bread.

9 See, for example, Susan E. Cayleff, *Wash and be Healed. The Water Cure Movement and Women's Health*, (Philadelphia, 1987), 118-120.

10 For a splendid fictionalised account of Kellogg, see T. Coraghessan Boyle, *The Road to Wellsville*, (London 1988).

11 Archibald Hunter Hygienic *Treatment for the Preservation of Health*, 3rd edn., 1897, advertisement p 15.

12 Metcalfe, op. cit. p. 190.

13 This information is drawn from the *National Archives of Scotland*, BT2/2/20, The Bridge of Allan Hydropathic Company.

14 *The Healthy Life and Hydropathic News*, November 1895, p.82.

15 Or *The British Physio-Medical Journal*. An organ advocating the teaching and Practice of Non-Poisonous Medication, Dietetics and Hygiene, based on the Vitalist Theory of Life. Vol X., No 5, May 1914, pp. 79-80.

16 *The Bridge of Allan Reporter* 24th April 1914 Death of Mrs Hunter, Agnes Steedman at Zetland House, after a long illness – widow of Dr Hunter and eldest daughter of John Anderson of Denham … ["numerous friends please accept of this as the only intimation".]

17 General Register House. Parish of Logie, 1914 485/B 2. 1914 April 24th at 6.15 am at Zetland House, Bridge of Allan, aged. 70. We are grateful to Mrs Elma Lindsay for a copy of this certificate.

18 *Scottish Cremation Society Register*, Maryhill Crematorium 1895-1916.

19 *National Archives of Scotland* SC 67/36/105 and inventory SC 67/36/150. Confirmation was granted on 28 October 1914; to her sister Annie Falshaw Anderson and two others.

Author Addresses
Alastair Dawson, Department of Geography, University of Coventry, CV1 5FB
G.A. Dixon, 3 Ronald Place, Stirling, FK8 1LF
Angela Douglas, Woodland Trust Scotland, Glenruthven Mill, Auchterarder, PH3 IDP
A.J. and C.E. Durie, 25 Forth Place, Stirling, FK8 1UD.
Noranne Ellis, Scottish Natural Heritage, 2 Anderson Place, Edinburgh, EH6 5EP
R.S. George, 54 Richmond Park Avenue, Bournemouth, BH8 9DR
John G. Harrison, 14a Abercromby Place, Stirling, FK8 2OP
S.J. Harrison, St. John's Vicarage, Main Street, Spittal, Berwick-upon-Tweed, TD15 1RP
C.J. Henty, Dept. of Psychology, University of Stirling, FK9 4LA
Peter Maitland, Fish Conservation Centre, Gladshot, Haddington, EH41 4NR
Ron Page, Kingarth, Airthrey Road, Stirling, FK9 5PH
Helen Smailes, National Gallery of Scotland, the Mound, Edinburgh, EH2 2EL
A. Thiel, 6 Tait Place, Tillicoultry, FK13 6RU

BOOK REVIEWS

Scotland for the Holidays; Tourism in Scotland, 1780 to 1939. Alastair Durie. Tuckwell Press. 206pp. ISBN 1 86232 121 3. £16.99.

FNH author's historic treatment is presented under heads – transport and tourism, seaside, search for health, sporting interest, WW1 and tourism, and the interwar period.

Stirling's Talking Stones. Elma Lindsay et al. Stirling Council Libraries. 60pp. ISBN 1 870 542 48 7. £2.

Well produced and illustrated accounts to introduce a few of the notable characters whose remains lie in the graveyards in the near vicinity of the Holy Rude Church. The selected 50, some of whom have been noted at times in the *Forth Naturalist and Historian*, are well presented with indexing and sources.

The Cairngorm Gateway. Ann Glen. Scottish Cultural Press. 336pp. ISBN 1 84017 027 1. £15.99.

Timely for the second Scottish National Park, this well researched and richly illustrated history of Badenoch and Strathspey includes the environmentally significant and scenic Rothiemurchus and Glenmore.

We have published a number of papers and reviews over the years on Robert Louis Stevenson, so some readers might be interested in this fine recent book which was featured in the exhibition and conference 'Navigating Stevenson' at the National Portrait Gallery early in the year –

Dreams of Elsewhere: selected worldwide travel writings of Robert Louis Stevenson. June Steiner Sawyer. The Pinn, Neil Wilson Publishing, Glasgow. 330pp. ISBN 1 9032338 62 5. £15.

Presented in sections related to – Scotland, England, France and Belgium, America, Switzerland, the South Seas, and miscellaneous – and with further reading notes. It includes his voyage to America, and so much more.

R. B. Cunninghame Graham: Fighter for Justice: an appreciation of his social and religious outlook. Ian M. Fraser. Ferndale, Gargunnock. 148pp. £8.99.

Shipping of the River Forth. William F. Henrie. Tempus. 128pp. ISBN 0 7524 2117 4. £12.99.

Well illustrated and researched, this work describes the historically once busy, river navigable to Stirling, in four chapters – upper and lower Forth, Leith and Granton, and the Firth.

THE FORTH NATURALIST AND HISTORIAN

The Forth Naturalist and Historian (FNH) is an informal enterprise of Stirling University. It was set up in 1975 by several University and Central Regional Council staff to provide a focus for interests, activities and publications of environmental, heritage and historical studies for the Forth area, comprising now local authority areas Stirling, Falkirk and Clackmannanshire.

The promotion of an annual environment/heritage symposium called *Man and the Landscape* has been a main feature, and this year, the 29th, it's on Water, Life and Landscape.

The annual *Forth Naturalist and Historian* has since 1975 published numerous papers, many being authoritative and significant in their field, and includes annual reports of the weather, and of birds in the locality, plus book reviews and notes. These volumes (26 as of 2003) provide a valuable successor to that basic resource *The Transactions of the Stirling Field and Archaeological Society, 1878-1939*. Four year contents/indexes are available, and selected papers are published in pamphlet form, while others e.g. The Weather and Bird Reports, are available as reprints.

A major publication is the 230 page *Central Scotland – Land, Wildlife, People* 1994, a natural history and heritage survey, and used in schools throughout the area, also in the form of a CD-Rom, *Heart of Scotland's Environment* (HSE).

Other FNH and associated publications still in print include – *Mines and Minerals of the Ochils, Airthrey and Bridge of Allan, Woollen Mills of the Hillfoots, The Ochil Hills* – landscape, wildlife, heritage – an introduction with walks, *Alloa Tower and the Erskines of Mar*, and the *Lure of Loch Lomond* a journey round the shores and islands. Several of these are in association with Clackmannanshire Field Studies Society. Godfrey Maps have collaborated in producing old Ordnance Survey large scale maps of the 1890s for 24 places in the area.

FNH publications are listed on the internet by Book Data (thebookplace.com), British Library (BLPC) and by booksellers e.g. Amazon, Bol, Barnes and Noble.

Offers of papers/notes for publication, and of presentations for symposia are ever welcome.

Honorary Secretary Lindsay Corbett,
University of Stirling, FK9 4LA, and 30 Dunmar Drive, Alloa, FK10 2EH.
Tel: 01259 215091. Fax: 01786 494994.
E-mail: lindsay.corbett@stir.ac.uk
Web: http://www.stir.ac.uk/departments/naturalsciences/Forth_naturalist